INTERNATIONAL SERIES OF MONOGRAPHS ON
ANALYTICAL CHEMISTRY

GENERAL EDITORS: R. BELCHER AND L. GORDON

Volume 20

NUCLEAR TECHNIQUES IN ANALYTICAL CHEMISTRY

NUCLEAR TECHNIQUES IN ANALYTICAL CHEMISTRY

by

ALFRED J. MOSES

Burbank, California

A Pergamon Press Book

THE MACMILLAN COMPANY

NEW YORK

THE MACMILLAN COMPANY
60 Fifth Avenue
New York 11, N.Y.

This book is distributed by
THE MACMILLAN COMPANY
pursuant to a special arrangement with
PERGAMON PRESS LIMITED
Oxford, England

First edition 1964

Library of Congress Catalog Card Number 64-15736

Set in Monotype Times 10 on 12 pt.
and printed in Great Britain by
Charles Birchall and Sons Ltd.,
Liverpool and London

CONTENTS

PREFACE

IN recent years, it has been recognized that micro-amounts of impurities or trace elements in systems can exert a profound influence on the biological, chemical, mechanical and physical properties of the system. With this realization there came a great demand for experimental determinations of these micro-amounts of material. The analytical chemist has become increasingly aware of the potentially high sensitivity of nuclear techniques. It is the function of this Monograph, to acquaint the analytical chemist with nuclear techniques, frequently combining older-established techniques with nuclear techniques to gain the desired sensitivity. In some cases, nuclear techniques are useful for the determination of macro-amounts of element, owing to the rapidity of a technique.

In closing, the author wishes to express his appreciation to scientists and engineers everywhere for their readiness to provide information, to his parents for their inspiration, and to his wife and son for their understanding.

ALFRED J. MOSES

Burbank, California

CHAPTER 1

SAFE HANDLING OF RADIOACTIVITY

WITH the increasingly frequent demand for the chemical determination of trace amounts of elements in materials, the analytical chemist had to search for more sensitive methods of analysis and had to evaluate other techniques for their applicability at trace levels. The phenomenon of radioactivity offered a means for detecting many elements at *part per million* and sometimes *part per billion* levels. The radioactivity is in some cases naturally occurring; in other cases it is artificially added.

The chemist, desiring to utilize nuclear techniques, must of course become familiar with properties of nuclear radiation and safe techniques for handling radioactivity. The following material will introduce very briefly the emission of radioactivity, to be followed by a discussion of various aspects of safe uses of radioactivity.

EMISSION OF RADIOACTIVITY

The principal radiations, emitted by radio-isotopes, are alpha and beta particles, neutrons and gamma rays. Pertinent properties of these radiations and particles are shown in Table 1.1. Several other modes of decay, such as internal conversion and electron

TABLE 1.1. NUCLEAR RADIATIONS AND PARTICLES

Radiation or particle	Symbol	Mass (atomic mass units)	Charge
Alpha	α	4	+2
Beta	$\beta-$	0.00055	−1
Positron	$\beta+$	0.00055	+1
Neutron	n	1	0
Gamma, X	γ, x	0	0

capture, are occasionally encountered; these processes are accompanied by the emission of electrons or X-rays. Isotopes and their more important nuclear properties are shown in Appendix A. Further information on nuclear properties is offered by texts on radiochemistry or nuclear physics [1-4].

UNITS OF RADIATION MEASUREMENT

Rate of Decay

Measurement of the rate of decay of a radio-isotope yields a quantity that is expressed as the *disintegration rate*. One curie is defined as the emission of 3.7×10^{10} disintegrations/sec. Subdivisions are microcurie (3.7×10^4 disintegrations/sec.) and the millicurie (3.7×10^7 disintegrations/sec). The disintegration rate, expressed in terms of curies or related units, measures only the number of atoms that disintegrate per second and gives no information concerning the type of radiation, particle, energies or contribution to the decay scheme. Therefore, the decay scheme must be consulted in determining the emission of a given radiation or particle.

Specific activities are expressed as disintegration rates per unit mass, such as curies per gram.

Radiation Dosage

The effect of radiation on matter and biological systems is the second measurement of interest. The basic unit is the *roentgen* (r), which is defined as "that quantity of γ-radiation required to produce ions having one electrostatic unit charge in one cubic centimeter of dry air under standard conditions." One roentgen will absorb 86 erg gram^{-1} of air or 97 erg gram^{-1} of tissue. Exposure dose rates are expressed in r hr^{-1} and mr hr^{-1}. The use of the roentgen is by definition limited to gamma (and X) radiation.

Absorbed doses of all types of nuclear radiation are expressed as *rad*, where one rad is an absorbed dose of 100 ergs g^{-1} of absorber. Absorbed dose rates are stated as rad hr^{-1} and millirad hr^{-1}.

The *roentgen equivalent man* (REM) is the quantity of any nuclear radiation which results in the same biological damage as one roentgen of gamma radiation.

Relative biological effectiveness (RBE) gives a measure of the damage to tissue from a given radiation, compared to damage from the absorption of one rad or gamma radiation.

The aforementioned quantities are interrelated by the definition: rad = REM/RBE. Table 1.2 states the RBE for various particles and radiations.

The permissible dose for workers, engaged in the use of radio-isotopes, is 5 REM per year or 0.1 REM per week. For the general population, the levels are one tenth of these values.

TABLE 1.2. RELATIVE BIOLOGICAL EFFECTIVENESS

Radiation or particle	RBE, equivalent to 1 REM
X or γ	1 r
$\beta+$ or $\beta-$	1 rad
Fast neutrons	0.1 rad
Protons, up to 10 MeV	0.1 rad
α, up to 7 MeV	0.1 rad
Heavy recoil nuclei	0.05 rad

Neutron dosages are often defined in terms of incident flux with 1 REM taken to equal 1.4×10^7 n cm^{-2}. The dosages are shown as a function of neutron energy in Table 1.3.

TABLE 1.3. REM FOR NEUTRONS

Neutron energy	n cm^{-2}, equivalent to 1 REM
0.025 eV (thermal)	9.6×10^8
0.001 MeV	4.8×10^8
0.01 MeV	4.6×10^8
0.1 MeV	0.96×10^8
0.5 MeV	0.38×10^8
1 MeV	0.29×10^8
2 MeV	0.19×10^8
3 MeV	0.14×10^8
>3 MeV	0.14×10^8

LICENSING

Most countries as well as their subdivisions have regulations governing the acquisition and use of many radio-isotopes. National regulatory agencies include:

United States of America: Division of Licensing and Regulation, U.S. Atomic Energy Commission, Washington 25, D.C.

Great Britain:
England:
Ministry of Housing & Local Government, Whitehall, London, S.W.1
Scotland:
Scottish Development Department, York Buildings, Queen Street, Edinburgh
Wales & Monmouthshire:
Ministry of Housing & Local Government, Cathays Park, Cardiff
Northern Ireland:
Ministry of Health & Local Government, Stormont, Belfast 4

Canada: Canadian Atomic Energy Control Board, c/o Atomic Energy of Canada Ltd., Commercial Products Division, P.O. Box 93, Ottawa

France: Commission Interministérielle des Radioéléments Artificels, Boîte postale No. 8, Gif-sur-Yvette (Seine-et-Oise)

In the United States of America, and possibly in other countries, certain small quantities of radioactive isotopes can be acquired and used without a formal license (Generally Licensed, sometimes erroneously called "License-Exempt"). Such quantities depend on the nuclear and biological properties of the radio-isotopes, and range in the U.S.A. from 0.1 to 250μc. Up to ten such quantities can be possessed but may not be combined. Many tracer studies can be performed with these generally-licensed amounts of activity. Some vendors of small amounts of radiotracers are listed in Table 2.1.

SHIELDING

In the analysis of highly radioactive materials, sample dissolution and dilutions are often performed remotely in a hot cell or

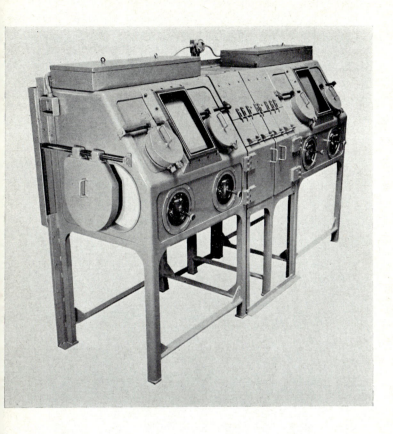

FIG. 1.1   Gamma box for handling radioactive materials
(Courtesy of Royal Research Corporation, Hayward, Calif.)

hot cave; somewhat lower levels of radioactivity are processed in a gamma box, as shown in Fig. 1.1. It is usually desirable to transfer a small aliquot of the solution to the chemistry laboratory, where the analysis can then be performed in the presence of relatively low levels of radiation. Alpha emitters, in the absence of major concentrations of fission product activity, are often handled in metal or plastic glove boxes[5-7].

In planning a radio-isotope experiment, advance estimates of radiation levels are best made and sufficient shielding arranged. In most cases, shielding for radiations other than gamma rays, can be neglected. The gamma output of radioactive sources is commonly expressed as r hr^{-1} at 1m (rhm). This quantity has been determined for many radio-isotopes and can be estimated for others in a manner shown later. Table 1.4 gives the gamma output per curie for some commonly used radio-isotopes.

TABLE 1.4. GAMMA OUTPUT OF RADIOACTIVE SOURCES

Radio-isotope	Gamma output (rhm c^{-1})	Radio-isotope	Gamma output (rhm c^{-1})
Sb^{124}	0.98	Ra^{226}	0.84
$Ce^{144} Pr^{144}$	0 035	Rb^{86}	0 051
Cs^{134}	0.82	Sc^{146}	1.1
Cs^{137}	0.32	Se^{75}	0.30
Co^{58}	0.54	Ag^{110}	1.4
Co^{60}	1.28	Na^{24}	1.84
Eu^{152}	0.55	Ta^{182}	0.61
Au^{198}	0.235	Tm^{170}	0.004
I^{131}	0.22	Sn^{113}	0.35
Ir^{192}	0.50	Zn^{65}	0.27
Fe^{59}	0.68	Zr^{95}	0.40
Hg^{203}	0.12		

If the gamma output per curie of a radio-isotope is not available, this quantity can be estimated using the formula:

$$R = 6C\bar{E}$$

where: R = output in r hr^{-1} at 1 ft
C = number of curies of activity
$\bar{E}$ = average photon energy per disintegration, MeV.

The transmission of a narrow beam of photons of energy E is expressed by

$$I = I_0 e^{-\mu x}$$

where: I = transmitted intensity
I_0 = incident intensity
μ = linear absorption coefficient, cm^{-1} or in^{-1}
x = thickness of intervening material, cm or in.

The linear absorption coefficients of some shielding materials are tabulated in Table 1.5

TABLE 1.5. LINEAR ABSORPTION COEFFICIENTS OF SOME MATERIALS

Gamma-ray energy, MeV	Materials and their linear absorption coefficients, cm^{-1}		
	Lead	Iron	Concrete
0.5	1.64	0.628	0.0870
1.0	0.774	0.452	0.0635
2.0	0.517	0.323	0.0445
3.0	0.476	0.275	0.0363

If the shielding requirement involves a broad beam of photons, the actual reduction in intensity of radiation by a shield will be less than the calculated value. In this case, a *buildup factor* as high as 10, may have to be applied. Calculations for broad beams of radiation are discussed in specialised texts on the subject.[8-9]

The *half-value thickness* is the thickness of shielding required to reduce the dose rate from I_0 to $I_{0/2}$. This value is equal to $0.693/\mu$.

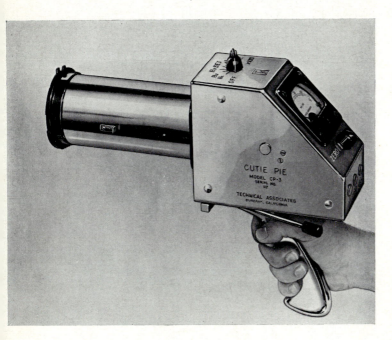

FIG. 1.2   Alpha–beta–gamma survey meter
(Courtesy of Technical Associates, Inc., Burbank, California)

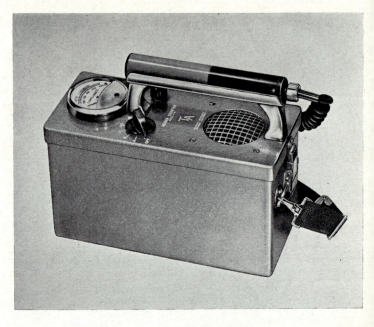

FIG. 1.3   Geiger–Müller type survey meter
(Courtesy of Technical Associates, Inc., Burbank, California)

Radiation levels in the laboratory are measured by means of ionization-type survey meters. Fig. 1.2 shows a high level alpha–beta–gamma survey meter. A Geiger–Müller type survey meter for lower levels of beta and gamma activity is shown in Fig. 1.3. The latter instrument is undoubtedly the best all purpose instrument as it is useful for monitoring personnel, laboratory surfaces, hands, etc. emitting from essentially no activity up to 20 mr hr^{-1}.

LABORATORY PRACTICES FOR HANDLING RADIO-ISOTOPES

The following rules will serve as a guide to chemists who are initiating radio-isotope experiments. Although the list may at a first glance look somewhat forbidding, closer inspection will reveal the common sense that governs the rules.

(1)   Obtain necessary licenses or permits to conduct the study.

(2)   Keep medical and safety authorities cognizant of your work.

(3)   Make an estimate of gamma ray dosage and use the most practical combination of distance, shielding and time to minimize personnel exposure; shielding usually consists of lead or iron bricks or concrete blocks. Measure dose rates with an appropriate radiation survey meter to assure adequacy of protection.

(4)   Perform all work with unsealed radio-isotopes on trays lined with absorbent material such as blotter paper.

(5)   Post radiation warning signs, as required by regulations.

(6)   Wear rubber gloves, film badge, a laboratory coat or overalls and shoe covers as necessary when handling radioactivity.

(7)   *Never* pipet radioactive solutions by mouth; use syringes or suction bulbs for this purpose.

(8)   Use properly labeled containers for disposal of liquid and solid radioactive wastes.

(9)   Use micropipets for preparing dilutions to minimize the generation of large volumes of waste solution.

(10)   Perform operations involving distillation, volatilization and evaporation of radioactive solutions in a fume hood.

(11)   Label containers holding radioactive materials and account for all such materials.

(12)   Use separate glassware for radioactive solutions.

(13)   Forbid eating, drinking, smoking and application of cosmetics while workers are located in the radio-isotope area.

(14)   Most importantly, use your common sense in planning and conducting your experiment.

MAXIMUM PERMISSIBLE LEVELS OF REMOVABLE CONTAMINATION

During and after an experiment, the area and equipment are usually examined for removable contamination. This test is commonly done by wiping a piece of filter paper over an area of 100 or 200 cm^2 and measuring the removed activity with a suitable counter. This test is called "smear," "wipe," or "swipe." The permissible limits of removable contamination depend on the degree of control of the area and the toxicity of the radio-isotope. Typical limits for removable activity from surfaces and clothing, in use in radioanalytical laboratories, are of the order of 10^{-5} μc cm^{-2} for alpha emitters and 10^{-4} μc cm^{-2} for beta emitters. Strontium–90 limits are generally the same as those for most alpha emitters.

2

RADIOACTIVE WASTE DISPOSAL

Radioactive waste disposal is a far more serious problem to the laboratory than is posed by other wastes. The short-lived isotopes are often stored until they have decayed to a sufficiently low level to permit disposal into sanitary sewers. Low-level solid wastes may be incinerated to reduce their bulk and the ashes disposed of as solid waste. Governmental authorities that authorize acquisition of radio-isotopes, can be consulted about channels for the disposal of higher level wastes.

DECONTAMINATION

If, in spite of all precautions, contamination has spread, the affected area should be roped off at once to prevent access by unauthorized people. A cleaning program is then initiated, starting with cleaning agents in the order shown below; there is no unanimity among experts concerning the best decontamination procedure. After each treatment, smears are taken to ascertain the level of decontamination, Suggested decontamination treatments are:

(1)   water containing a detergent;
(2)   water containing a complexing agent such as EDTA and possibly inactive carriers;
(3)   appropriate acids, organic solvents, sand blasting, etc.

In all cases, knowledge of the spilled element aids in devising adequate decontamination procedures. Waste solutions must be disposed of in the proper manner, dependent on their activity level.

TOXICITY

The toxicity hazard from radio-isotopes is due to the biological damage that radiation can induce in a person following incorporation in the body. Radio-isotopes have been graded on the basis of their toxicity. The highest toxicity is assigned to most alpha emitters and strontium–90. The toxicity classification of radio-isotopes and their maximum permissible concentrations in air and water have been tabulated [10,11].

PYROPHORICITY

The pyrophoricity of some materials can create both a fire hazard and a contamination hazard. Although the analytical chemist may not normally encounter this hazard, it must be kept in mind when working with powdered metals, as well as with hydrides and carbides of the actinides. The use of open flames is not advisable around radio-isotopes as this may lead to contamination.

NUCLEAR CRITICALITY

Nuclear criticality is a hazard only when working with quantities of some actinides on at least a gram scale. The author's text[12] on actinides offers more detailed information concerning this hazard.

REFERENCES

1. B. S. DZHELEPOV and C. K. PEKER, *Decay Schemes of Radioactive Nuclei*, Pergamon Press, New York (1961).
2. D. STROMINGER, J. M. HOLLANDER and G. T. SEABORG, *Rev. Mod. Phys.*, **30**, 585 (1958).
3. W. H. SULLIVAN, *Trilinear Chart of Nuclides*, 2nd Ed., U.S. Government Printing Office, Washington, 1957; and suppl.
4. J. F. STEHN, *Nucleonics* **18**, No. 11, 186 (1960).
5. G. E. WALTON (Ed.), *Glove Boxes and Shielded Cells for Handling Radioactive Materials*, Butterworths, London (1958).
6. C. F. METZ and G. R. WATERBURY, *Talanta* **6**, 149 (1960).
7. V. GRIFFITHS, U.K. A.E.R.E. Report No. AHSB(S)R18 (1962).
8. B. T. PRICE, C. C. HORTON and K. T. SPINNEY, *Radiation Shielding*, Pergamon Press, New York (1958).
9. H. ETHERINGTON (Ed.), *Nuclear Engineering Handbook*, McGraw-Hill, New York (1958).
10. *A Basic Toxicity Classification of Radionuclides*, Technical Report Series No. 15, International Atomic Energy Agency, Vienna (1963).
11. *Maximum Permissible Body Burdens and Maximum Permissible Concentrations of Radionuclides in Air and in Water for Occupational Exposure*, Handbook No. 69, U.S. National Bureau of Standards, Washington (1959).
12. A. J. MOSES, *Analytical Chemistry of the Actinide Elements*, Pergamon Press, Oxford (1963).

CHAPTER 2

NUCLEAR INSTRUMENTATION, SOURCES OF RADIATION AND RADIOCHEMICAL TECHNIQUES

NUCLEAR techniques are based on the use of a source of radio-activity and the detection of its radiation. Chemical operations are frequently required to prepare materials, prior to measurement of the desired radiation. This chapter lays the basis for a discussion of the application of nuclear techniques to analytical chemistry by a discussion of:

(1) the nature of radioactivity,
(2) interaction of radiation with matter,
(3) principles of radiation detection,
(4) sources of radiation,
(5) radiochemical techniques and
(6) nuclear instrumentation.

THE NATURE OF RADIOACTIVITY

The decay of a radio-isotope is frequently accompanied by emission of one or more of the following radiations: alpha particles, beta particles, and photons (X- and γ-rays).

The rate of decay obeys the law:
$$dN/dt = -\lambda N$$
where: λ = decay constant = $0.693/T$
T = half-life of radioactivity
N = number of radioactive atoms of half-life T
Integration between the limits $t = O$ and $t = t$, yields:
$$N_t = N.e^{-\lambda t}$$

Activity, A, is defined as: $A = -\lambda N$ hence, $A_t = A.e^{-\lambda t}$ and where

A = initial activity, in dpm or dps.*

*See Appendix F for abbreviations.

Owing to the exponential nature of radioactive decay, a plot of *activity* vs. *time* will give a straight line on semilogarithmic paper if only one radio-isotope is present. If several radio-isotopes are present, their contributions to the composite decay curve can be determined by subtraction, provided the half-lives differ appreciably. Figure 2.1 presents a composite decay curve with contributions

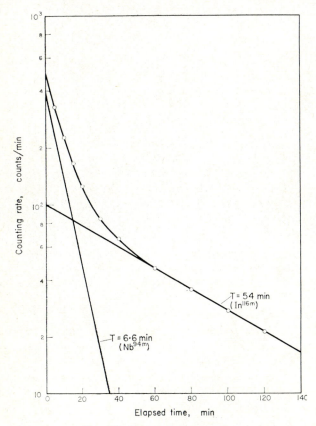

FIG. 2.1   Composite decay curve

from In^{116m} and Nb^{94m}. These contributions are resolved by drawing a straight line on the composite decay curve, starting with the longest elapsed time and ending at zero time. This line represents the decay of the longest-lived component, In^{116m}. Then elapsed times of 0, 5, 10, 20 and 30 min are selected and the appropriate In^{116m} contribution subtracted from the counting rate of the composite curve. The resultant counting rates are plotted on the same paper. A line drawn through these points represents the decay of the shorter-lived component, Nb^{94m}. The half-life of a component is determined by noting the counting rate at time = 0 min, then following the line to half the counting rate, and reading off the corresponding time. Thus, the line from the decay of In^{116m} gives a counting rate of 100 cpm at time = 0 min; at 50 cpm, a time = 54 min is read off. The half-life is thus 54 min.

INTERACTION OF RADIATION WITH MATTER

Alpha particles dissipate their energy in passing through matter mainly by interaction with electrons, causing the formation of ions. The range of alpha particles is short, a few centimeters in air and a few microns in metals.

Beta particles (electrons) lose their energy by ionization and by emission of radiation. and by emission of radiation. The latter, called "Bremsstrahlung," occurs when an electron is decelerated in the electric field of a nucleus and manifests itself as X-radiation. This effect is most pronounced where absorbers of high atomic number are involved (e.g. lead).

Gamma rays and X-rays interact with matter in three ways:

(1) by the *photo-electric effect*, in which the whole energy is transferred to an orbital electron;

(2) by the *Compton effect*, in which an elastic collision takes place with an electron and a reduction of gamma-ray energy results;

(3) by *pair production*, in which a positron–electron pair is created with each particle having a mass equivalent to 0.51 MeV. The minimum energy for this process is thus 1.02 MeV. The gamma-ray energy in excess of this amount is imparted to the two particles as kinetic energy.

At low gamma-ray energies, in high Z absorbers, the photo-electric effect is predominant. The Compton effect predominates at medium energies, while the pair production becomes important in high Z materials for high gamma energies.

The linear absorption coefficient, cited in Chapter I, is the sum of the coefficients for these three processes.

PRINCIPLES OF RADIATION DETECTION

The types of radiations, most commonly encountered, have been discussed earlier. Alpha particles are emitted almost exclusively by elements above lead in atomic number. Their energy is usually between 4 and 6 MeV. The short range of alpha particles permits highly efficient counting of these particles in windowless-gas flow proportional counters and scintillation counters with zinc sulfide phosphors. Owing to the discrete energy of alpha particles, alpha spectrometry is a relatively common practice. Scintillation spectrometers, grid chambers, and solid state ionization chambers are used for this purpose. Information on counting equipment is discussed later in this chapter.

Beta particles are emitted by many nuclides, but owing to the continuous shape of beta spectra, beta spectrometry is difficult and usually omitted in favor of gamma spectrometry. Fig. 2.2 shows a typical beta spectrum. The spectra are characterized by the maximum energy, E_{max}, which is the value indicated in Appendix A.

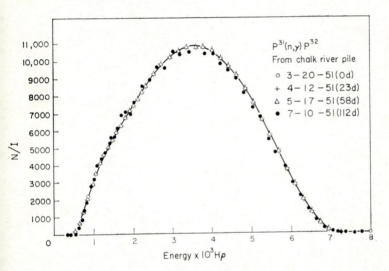

FIG. 2.2   Beta spectrum of P^{32}

(From E. N. JENSEN, R. T. NICHOLS, J. CLEMENT and A. POHM, U.S. Atomic Energy Comm. Rep. ISC–157 (1951))

E_{max} is difficult to determine with high accuracy because of Bremsstrahlung. Generally, aluminum absorbers of various thicknesses are inserted between the source and counter, best nearest to the counter, and the counting rate determined. A plot of *log counting rate* vs. *absorber thickness in mg/cm²* is usually constructed. In the absence of gamma radiation and Bremsstrahlung, a visual estimate can sometimes be made of the maximum range of the beta particles. Then, with the graph of *beta energy* vs. *range*, Fig. 2.3, the maximum beta energy is established. In less favorable circumstances,

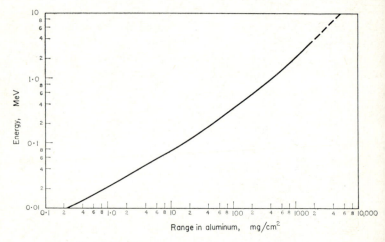

Fig. 2.3*   Range–energy relation for beta particles

the fractional absorption of the unknown beta emitter is compared to that of a known beta source and E_{max} determined. The "Feather Plot" follows this approach.[1-3]

Beta counting is commonly performed with Geiger–Müller counters. Here the determination of the absolute disintegration rate of a beta emitter is not a simple matter. Factors that merit consideration include:

(1)   counting geometry,
(2)   self-absorption of radiation in sample,
(3)   absorption of radiation by intervening air,
(4)   absorption of radiation by counter window,
(5)   backscatter of radiation by the source mounting and walls of counting shield and
(6)   contributions from gamma radiation and Bremsstrahlung.

*After L. E. GLENDENIN, *Nucleonics* **1**, 31 (1948).

Owing to the complexicity of absolute beta counting, it is recommended that appropriate standard solutions be purchased and counting samples be prepared, in a manner similar to the sample to be counted. A comparison of counting rates will then permit accurate determination of disintegration rates. Sources of standard solutions are listed in Table 2.1.

Low energy beta particles are frequently counted in liquid scintillation counters, where some energy discrimination is possible. Thus, C^{14} can be counted in the presence of H^3.

The windowless proportional counters are quite suitable for beta counting but it is more difficult to obtain absorption curves with these counters. Further, volatile materials can not be counted in such counters.

TABLE 2.1 BETA AND GAMMA STANDARD SOLUTIONS

Nuclide	Half-life	Type of standard		E_{max} MeV	γ-energy, MeV	Suppliers
		beta	gamma			
H^3	12.5 years	x		0.018		1, 2, 3, 6
Ni^{63}	85 years	x		0.067		2
C^{14}	5568 years	x		0.155		2, 4, 6
S^{35}	87.1 days	x		0.167		2, 4, 7
Co^{60}	5.27 years	x	x	0.312	1.17, 1.33	2, 4, 5, 7
Cs^{137}	29.6 years	x	x	0.52, 1.17	0.032, 0.662	2, 4, 7
$Sr-Y^{90}$	28 years	x		0.54, 2.27		2, 4, 5
Tl^{204}	3.9 years	x		0.77		2, 4
$Pb-Bi^{210}$	22 years	x		1.16		2.4
P^{32}	14.6 days	x		1.71		2, 4, 5, 7
Cd^{109}	1.3 years		x		0.088	2, 8
Co^{57}	270 days		x		0.123	2, 4, 8
Hg^{203}	47 days		x	0.21	0.279	1, 2
Mn^{54}	300 days		x		0.840	1, 2, 8
Sc^{46}	83.9 days		x	0.36	0.89, 1.12	1, 2
Zn^{65}	245 days		x	$\beta+$	0.51, 1.12	1, 2, 4
Na^{22}	2.6 years		x	$\beta+$	0.51, 1.28	1, 2, 8

1. National Bureau of Standards, U.S. Dept. of Commerce, Washington 25, D.C., U.S.A.
2. United Kingdom Atomic Energy Authority, The Radiochemical Centre, Amersham, Buckinghamshire, England.
3. New England Nuclear Corp., 575 Albany St., Boston 18, Mass., U.S.A.
4. Nuclear-Chicago Corp., 333 East Howard Ave., Des Plaines, Ill., U.S.A.
5. The National Physical Laboratory, Teddington, Middlesex, England.

6. Tracerlab, Inc., 1601 Trapelo Road, Waltham 54, Mass., U.S.A.
7. Commissariat a l'Énérgie Atomique, Gif-sur-Yvette (Seine-et-Oise), France.
8. Nuclear Science and Engineering Corp., Box 10901, Pittsburgh 36, Pa.,
    U.S.A.

In addition to standard solutions, many of the listed firms provide
solid standard sources. Additional suppliers of solid standards
include:

N.V. Philips-Duphar, Amsterdam, Holland.
Atomic Accessories, Inc., 811 W. Merrick Rd., Valley Stream, N.Y., U.S A.

Many techniques, described in this monograph, employ radiotracers. Table 2.2 lists some commonly used tracers and their
nuclear properties. The reader is referred to Table 2.1 for a list
of suppliers of such tracer solutions.

Photons (X-rays and gamma-rays) have discrete energies. Prior
to the advent of scintillation spectrometry, the energy of photons
was usually determined by absorption in materials of high atomic
number, such as lead and tantalum. Now, gamma scintillation
spectometry with thallium-activated sodium iodide or cesium
iodide crystals has been widely accepted as the method of choice.
Gamma emitters frequently emit gamma rays of several energies.
Information concerning gamma spectra of many nuclides has been
assembled by several authors.[4-6] Fig. 2.4 shows a gamma spectrum
from the decay of Al^{28}. This nuclide decays by beta emission to Si^{28},
followed by emission of a 1.78 MeV gamma ray. The 1.78 MeV
photopeak represents full absorption of the primary photon, while
the other phenomena are due to scattering of the primary photons.
Bremsstrahlung is caused by beta radiation.

The reduction of complex spectra may be accomplished by
successive subtraction of the gamma spectra due to each nuclide,
starting with the photopeak of highest energy. This subtraction
process may be done graphically using a semi-logarithmic plot,[7]
or by a "complementing" technique with a multi-channel analyzer.[8]
Photoelectric efficiencies for standard sizes of sodium iodide
crystals have been tabulated by several workers[4,6]. Standards are
useful for energy calibration and absolute calibration of gamma
counters. The standard solutions and solid standards may be
obtained from the firms listed in Table 2.1. The preparation of solid
standards has been discussed by several workers.[9,10]

TABLE 2.2. LIST OF SOME USEFUL RADIOTRACERS

Isotope	Half-life	β	γ, x	Other	Isotope	Half-life	β	γ, x	Other
	12.46y	*			Cd^{115m}	43d	*	*	
	53d		*		In^{114m}	49d–72s	*	*	EC, IT
	5568y	*			Sn^{113}	115d		*	EC
22	2.6y	*+	*		Sb^{122}	67h	*	*	EC
	14.3d	*			Sb^{124}	60d	*	*	
	87.1d	*			I^{125}	57·4d		*	EC
6	3.2×10⁵y	*			I^{131}	8.05d	*	*	
2	12.7h	*	*		Xe^{133}	5.27d	*	*	
15	164d	*			Cs^{134}	2.3y	*	*	
6	85d	*	*		Cs^{137}–Ba^{137m}	29.2y–2.6m	*	*	
1	27.8d		*	EC	Ba^{133}	7.2y		*	EC
54	310d		*	EC	Ba^{140}–La^{140}	12.8d–40h	*	*	
5	2.94y		*	EC	La^{140}	40h	*	*	
9	45.1d	*	*		Ce^{141}	32.5d	*	*	
57	270d	*+	*		Ce^{144}–Pr^{144}	290d–17·5m	*	*	
58	72d	*+	*	EC	Pr^{142}	19.3h	*	*	
50	5.27y	*	*		Nd^{147}–Pm^{147}	11.3d–2.6y	*	*	
3	125y	*			Pm^{147}	2.6y	*		
54	12.8h	*+	*	EC	Sm^{153}	47h	*	*	
55	245d	*+	*	EC	Eu^{152,154}	12.7y, 16y	*	*	EC
72	14.2h	*	*		Tb^{160}	73d	*	*	
71	11.4d			EC	Ho^{166}	27h	*	*	
6	26.6h	*	*		Er^{169}	9.4d	*		
5	127d		*	EC	Tm^{170}	127d	*	*	
2	35.87h	*	*		Lu^{177}	6.75d	*	*	
35	10.27y	*	*		Hf^{181}	46d	*	*	
36	18.6d	*	*		Ta^{182}	112d	*	*	
5	65d		*		W^{185}	74d	*		
	53d	*			Re^{186}	91h	*	*	
–Y^{90}	28y–64.2h	*			Os^{191}	16d	*	*	
	105d	*+	*	EC	Ir^{192}	74.5d	*	*	EC
	64.2h	*			Au^{198}	65h	*	*	
	58.0d	*	*		Hg^{203}	46d	*	*	
5–Nb^{95}	63.3d–35d	*	*		Tl^{204}	4.1y	*		
95	35d	*	*		Pb^{210}	22y	*	*	
99	67h	*	*		Bi^{210}	5.02d	*		
97	69.6h		*	EC	Po^{210}	138d			α
103	41.0d	*	*		Th^{228}	1.91y		*	α
106–Rh^{106}	1.0y–30s	*	*		U^{233}	1.62×10⁵y		*	α
109	13.6h	*	*		Pu^{236}	2.7y		*	α,CE
110m	270d	*	*		Pu^{238}	85.59y		*	α, SF
111	7.5d	*	*		Pu^{242}	3.8×10⁵y		*	α, SF
109	1.3y		*	EC					

Notes:
1.   + after asterisk, under β, indicates decay by positron emission.

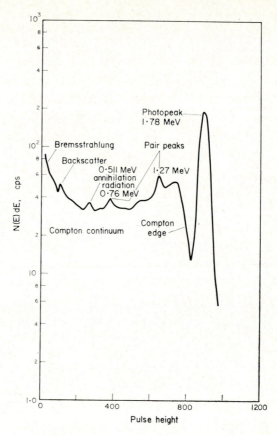

FIG. 2.4*   Gamma spectrum from 2.3 min Al^{28} (3in. × 3in.– .NaI Phosphor, absorber 1.34 g/cm² Be, source distance 10 cm, energy scale 2 keV/PHU)

The Statistics of Counting. Radioactive decay occurs in a random manner, resulting in some uncertainty concerning the time at which the decay occurred. Therefore, laws of statistics must be used to express the probability of the occurrence of a disintegration.

As discussed elsewhere, [1,11−15] counting statistics are best expressed by the Gaussian approximation, also called the "Standard Distribution Curve." The width of this curve is indicated by the "variance" calculated by averaging the squares of the deviations

*After R. L. HEATH, IDO–16408.

from the mean. The standard deviation, σ_x, is the square root of the variance. Table 2.3 presents typical counting data with variances and standard deviations.

TABLE 2.3. STATISTICAL INTERPRETATION OF DATA

Test No.	Number of counts, N	Deviation from mean	(Deviation, etc.)^2
1	90	-10	100
2	100	0	0
3	110	$+10$	100
	Total 300	0	200

(Mean = 100)

Here, $\sigma_x^2 = 200/3 = 66.7$ from which $\sigma_x = 8.18$.
The result is then $100 \pm \sigma_x$ counts, or 100 ± 8.2 counts.

In this example, $1\sigma_x$ was used. This deviation represents 68.3 per cent probability that the result will be within $\pm\sigma_x$, i.e., between 92 and 108 counts. If the limit is set as $1.96\,\sigma_x$, then the result will be correct 95 per cent of the time.

Table 2.4 shows the relation between the number of standard deviations and the confidence limit.

TABLE 2.4. CONFIDENCE LIMITS

Number of standard deviations σ	Probability (confidence limit), $\%$
$0.50 \times \sigma$	38.3
$0.68 \times \sigma$	50.0
$1.00 \times \sigma$	68.3
$1.96 \times \sigma$	95.0
$2.58 \times \sigma$	99.0
$3.00 \times \sigma$	99.7

Counting results are usually expressed as rates, i.e., events per unit time. Where relatively low counting rates are obtained, allowance must be made for the background activity (blank). The standard deviation is then:

$$\sigma = (\sigma_x^2 + \sigma_b^2)^{1/2}$$

where: $\sigma = \dfrac{(N)^{1/2}}{t}$

The following example offers a sample calculation:

$$
\begin{aligned}
\text{Total counts} &= 1600 \\
\text{Counting time} &= 10 \text{ min} \\
\text{Counting rate} &= 1600/10 = 160 \text{ cpm} \\
\sigma_x &= \pm \frac{(1600)^{\frac{1}{2}}}{10} = \pm 4 \text{ cpm}
\end{aligned}
$$

$$
\begin{aligned}
\text{Background counts} &= 900 \\
\text{Counting time} &= 20 \text{ min} \\
\text{Counting rate} &= 900/20 = 45 \text{ cpm} \\
\sigma_b &= \pm \frac{(900)^{\frac{1}{2}}}{20} = \pm 1.5 \text{ cpm}
\end{aligned}
$$

The net activity of the sample is then $160-45 = 115$ cpm, and the net standard deviation, $\sigma = [(4)^2 + (1.5)^2]^{\frac{1}{2}} = \pm 4.3$ cpm. The activity of the sample, with standard deviation of $1\,\sigma$, is thus (115 ± 4.3) cpm.

It is not within the scope of this monograph to discuss the many applications of statistics to the measurement of radioactivity. The references cited provide adequate information for the analytical chemist.

SOURCES OF RADIATION

Activation analysis and frequently the preparation of suitably labeled tracers involve the use of radiation sources. For convenience, the latter are divided here into the following three categories:

(1) Isotopic sources
(2) Accelerators
(3) Nuclear reactors.

These types of radiation sources will now be briefly reviewed. (Additional information is offered in the analytical procedures in the appropriate chapters in this monograph.)

Radiations from radio-isotope sources may be used in conjunction with material of suitable threshold and cross-section to produce neutrons.

Analytical applications for alpha sources include the determination of beryllium and of film thicknesses.

The application of beta sources to analytical chemistry is confined to transmission, absorption, backscattering, and as a source of X-rays by Bremsstrahlung. (These applications are not discussed in this monograph.)

Gamma sources are used to measure the concentration of heavy elements such as actinides by absorption,[16] and to analyze for beryllium and deuterium by photo-activation.

Neutrons can be produced either by (α, n) reactions with Po^{210}, Ra^{226}, Pu^{239}, Am^{241} or by (γ, n) reactions with Ra^{226} and Sb^{124}. Beryllium, boron and deuterated materials have been used as targets for these neutron-producing reactions, with beryllium producing the most prolific neutron output. Owing to the short range of alpha particles, the alpha emitters and target material (e.g., beryllium), must be intimately mixed. The (α, n) reactions are preferred as they give a higher neutron yield and require far less shielding.

Table 2.5 lists isotopic neutron sources and some of their characteristics.

TABLE 2.5. ISOTOPIC NEUTRON SOURCES

Source	Reaction	Half-life		Neutron energy, MeV	Approximate Neutron flux, n sec^{-1} curie^{-1}
Ra–Be	α, n	1622	years	<13	1.5×10^7
Po^{210}–Be	α, n	138	days	<11	2.5×10^6
Pu^{239}–Be	α, n	24360	years	<11	2.2×10^6
Sb^{124}–Be	γ, n	60	days	0.024	1.9×10^5
Cf^{252}	spont. fission	2.2	years	< 9	2.6×10^{12} n sec^{-1} g^{-1}

As may be seen from Table 2.5, spontaneous fission can produce large neutron outputs; however, such sources are not yet available to most chemists. Isotopic neutron sources are used in activation analysis of elements with high neutron activation cross sections and in the analysis of some elements by absorption and scattering.

Isotopic neutron sources are frequently surrounded by a hydrogenous moderator such as paraffin or water, to provide the more useful thermal neutron flux. Such an assembly is often called a *neutron howitzer* and is shown in Fig. 2.5.

Accelerators are used in a number of determinations of elements utilizing positive ion bombardment, photonuclear reactions, as well as fast and thermal neutron reactions. Much of the early work was performed with cyclotrons and suitable proton or deuteron-induced reactions. With cyclotrons it is possible to obtain reactor-level neutron fluxes over small volumes. Van de Graaff

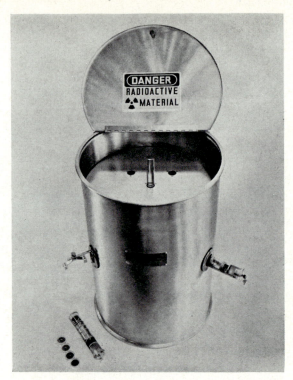

FIG. 2.5   Neutron howitzer
(Courtesy of Nuclear-Chicago Corp., Des Plaines, Ill.

positive ion accelerators are used in a similar manner to cyclotrons, although the energy of the radiations is much lower. Van de Graaff electron accelerators and Betatrons accelerate electrons which are allowed to react with X-ray producing targets such as gold; the X-rays, in turn, produce neutrons by photonuclear reaction with a target such as beryllium. In recent years, the Cockroft–Walton positive ion accelerators have come into wide use as a source of fast and thermal neutrons; the latter occur from use of a moderator for the fast neutrons, resulting from the reaction H^3 (d, n)He^4.

Fig. 2.6 shows a typical Cockroft–Walton accelerator, used in fast neutron activation analysis. An installation layout for such an accelerator is shown in Fig. 2.7.

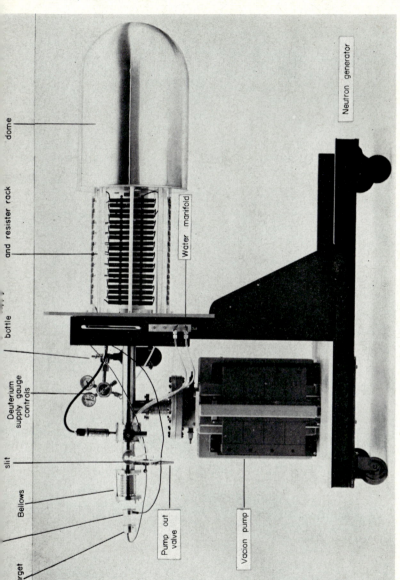

dome

and resister rack

Water manifold

bottle

Deuterium supply gauge controls

slit

Bellows

Pump out valve

Target

Neutron generator

Vacion pump

Fig. 2.6 Cockroft–Walton accelerator
(Courtesy of Nuclear-Chicago Corp., Des Plaines, Ill.)

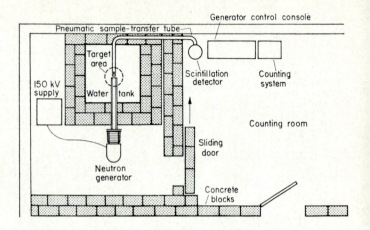

FIG. 2.7   Installation of Cockroft–Walton accelerator
(Courtesy of Nuclear-Chicago Corp., Des Plaines, Ill.)

The neutron-induced fission of U^{235} in a nuclear reactor is the most widely used source of high neutron fluxes. Many types of reactors are used by chemists for activation analysis. A small

TABLE 2.6. PROPERTIES OF SOME NEUTRON SOURCES

Source, accelerating voltage, and reaction	Typical neutron flux density, n cm^{-2} sec^{-1}	
	Fast—14 MeV	Thermal—0.025 eV
Reactor: U^{235} fission	—	10^8–10^{15}
Van de Graaff accelerator, 3 MeV, Be^9(d, n)	5×10^8	5×10^9
Cyclotron; 8 MeV, Be^9 (d, n)	1×10^{10}	1×10^{11}
Cockroft–Walton generator; 0.15 MeV, H^3 (d, n)	4×10^9	5×10^8
Betatron; 80 MeV, U (e, n)	—	1×10^8
Sealed Tube Source; 0.15 MeV, H^3 (d, n)	1×10^5	5×10^3
Pu–Be Source; 1 c, Be^9 (α, n)	—	2×10^4
Ra–Be Source; 1 c, Be^9 (α, n)	—	1×10^5
Sb^{124}–Be Source; 1 c, Be^9 (γ, n)	—	2×10^3

laboratory reactor with a thermal neutron flux of 2×10^8 n cm^{-2} sec^{-1} is shown in Fig. 2.8; a larger reactor, producing fluxes of 2×10^{12} n cm^{-2} sec^{-1} is presented in Fig. 2.9.

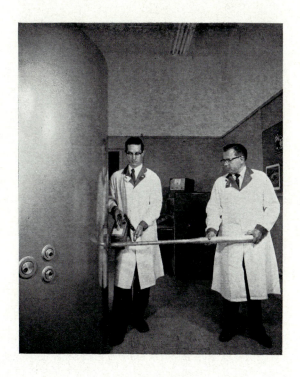

FIG. 2.8   Low–flux laboratory reactor
(Courtesy of Atomics International, Div. of North American Aviation Inc., Canoga Park, Calif.)

As has been previously indicated, many analytical requirements can be met by the employment of isotopic neutron sources, small accelerators and low power reactors. Irradiations in high flux reactors often necessitate the use of hot cells or other shielded facilities for processing of irradiated specimens. Table 2.6 lists the properties of various types of neutron sources.

FIG. 2.9   Swimming pool type nuclear reactor
(Courtesy of General Atomic Div., General Dynamics Corp., San Diego, Calif.)

RADIOCHEMICAL TECHNIQUES

Radiochemical techniques are the basis of the application of nuclear techniques to inorganic analysis. In view of the broad scope of radiochemical techniques, they are presented throughout the monograph as a part of analytical procedures. For a more formal treatment, the reader is referred to several texts[1,2,17,18] and to the excellent set of manuals, published by the Subcommittee on Radiochemistry, National Academy of Sciences-National Research Council.[19]

NUCLEAR INSTRUMENTATION

Radiation detectors in common use by analytical chemists, are divided into three broad categories:

(1)   Ionization devices, including ion chambers, proportional counters, Geiger-Müller counters, and solid state ionization chambers.

(2)   Scintillation counters.

(3)   Photographic emulsions.

The operation of a gas-filled counter as an ion chamber, proportional counter or Geiger–Müller counter is determined by the operating voltage. Fig. 2.10 presents the characteristic operating voltages of these devices.[20] Several types of Geiger–Müller counters are shown in Fig. 2.11. The Geiger–Müller counters are

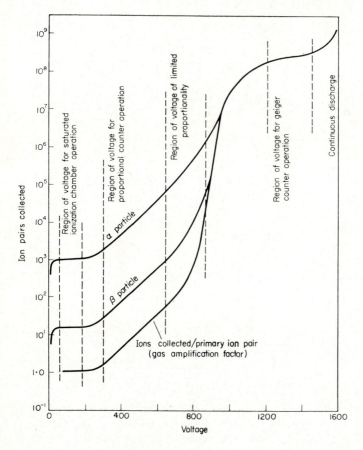

FIG. 2.10   Characteristics of an idealized counter as a function of voltage

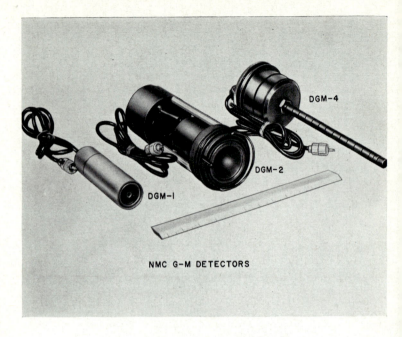

FIG. 2.11   Geiger–Müller detectors
(Courtesy of Nuclear Measurements Corp., Indianapolis, Ind.)

used mainly for beta counting. Windowless proportional gas flow counters are used for the detection of alpha and beta particles. Their short dead time, versatility and relative freedom from difficult counting corrections makes these gas flow counters highly desirable. Fig. 2.12 illustrates a windowless proportional gas flow counter with scaling circuit. The sample is placed on a tray of the sliding counting chamber. The counter is shown in the "operate" position. Ionization chambers are used for monitoring relatively high levels of radiation. Fig. 1.2 shows an instrument, incorporating an ion chamber. In addition, alpha spectra can be obtained with a "Frisch Grid Chamber," shown in Figs. 2.13 and 2.14.

In recent years, solid state ionization devices have found application in the detection of beta particles, alpha particles, positive ions and fission fragments. Although their application in the field of analytical chemistry has been limited to a modest amount of work

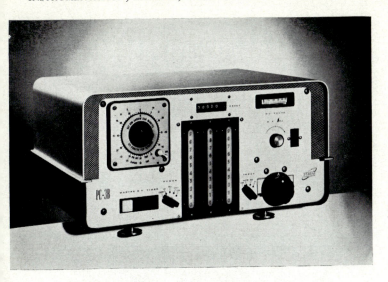

FIG. 2.12   Windowless proportional flow counter with scaler
(Courtesy of Nuclear Measurements Corp., Indianapolis, Ind.)

in alpha spectrometry, the excellent resolution of the devices, their relatively low cost, and ease of use will undoubtedly result in their eventual wide usage. The principles of solid state detectors have been described by a number of authors.[21-24]

The detection devices such as counters must employ suitable electronic circuits to convert the very small currents in detectors to an intelligible message. Fig. 2.15 presents the block diagrams showing major components of some counting systems.

It was indicated earlier that Geiger–Müller counters show a relatively slow recovery time after the initial ionization event. The resultant "dead time" or resolving time ranges from 50 to 500 μsec with a typical value of 200 μsec. This is expressed by the equation[25]

$$n_t = \frac{n_0}{1 - n_0 \tau}$$

where: n_t = observed counting rate, counts/sec.
n_0 = true counting rate, counts/sec.
τ = resolving time, sec.

The resolving time is frequently determined by the use of paired (split) sources, where each half has the same activity. Another

FIG. 2.13   Detail view of Frisch grid chamber
(Courtesy of Eberline Instrument Co., Santa Fe, New Mexico)

FIG. 2.14   Complete Frisch grid counting system
(Courtesy of Eberline Instrument Co., Santa Fe, New Mexico)

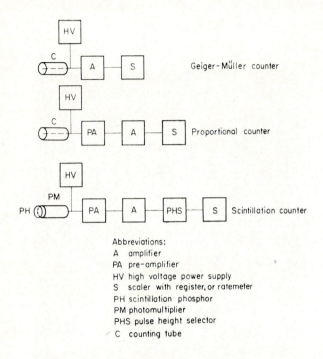

Abbreviations:
A   amplifier
PA pre-amplifier
HV high voltage power supply
S   scaler with register, or ratemeter
PH scintillation phosphor
PM photomultiplier
PHS pulse height selector
C   counting tube

FIG. 2.15   Block diagrams of some counting systems

echnique measures the resolving time electronically on an oscillo-cope with triggered sweep.[26]

The interaction of radioactivity with certain phosphors will produce pulses of light. These pulses of light are converted to electric current and amplified by photomultiplier tubes. The electric current in the photomultiplier tube is proportional to the energy osses suffered by the radiation in the phosphor. The scintillation counter is therefore capable of measuring the energy distribution of radiation (spectrum) and the intensity as a function of energy. Fig. 2.15 contains a block diagram of a scintillation spectrometer. Fig. 2.4 shows a gamma spectrum, redrawn from a report by Heath.[6] A typical single-channel gamma ray spectrometer is shown in Fig. 2.16. Gamma scintillation spectrometry is used widely in analytical applications, owing to the possibility of typify-

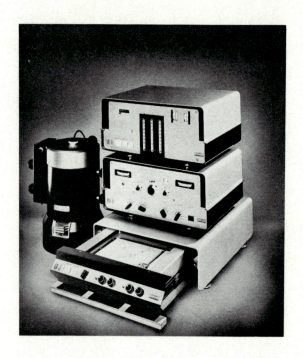

FIG. 2.16   Single channel gamma ray spectrometer
(Courtesy of Nuclear Measurements Corp., Indianapolis, Ind.)

ing radionuclides by their characteristic spectra and the relative freedom from cumbersome counting corrections. Solid, thallium-activated sodium iodide crystals, both with and without sample-containing cavity "well," are commonly-used gamma ray counters. Anthracene crystals find occasional use in beta counting.

Zinc sulfide phosphors are employed in alpha counting.

A typical liquid scintillation counter for beta counting is shown in Fig. 2.17. Techniques of gamma scintillation counting have been

iscussed by Crouthamel[4] and of liquid scintillation counting
by Bell and Hayes.[27]

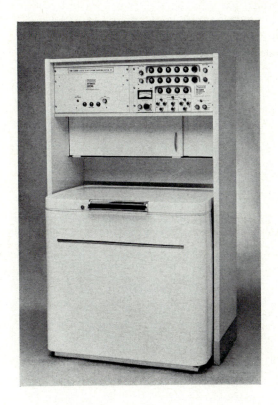

FIG. 2.17 Liquid scintillation spectrometer
(Courtesy of Packard Instrument Co., La Grange, Ill.)

Ionizing radiation will cause activation of silver halide in photographic emulsions, resulting in a visible black deposit of metallic
silver upon development. The use of nuclear emulsions (auto-
radiography) for the detection of radiation in analytical chemistry
is largely confined to the determination of very low alpha disintegration rates for health physics purposes. Details on a number
of applications of emulsion techniques are offered by Yagoda[28]

and Norris and Woodruff.[29] A typical procedure for the deter
mination of plutonium in urine is described by Moses.[16]

The spectra shown in this monograph were obtained with the aid of puls
height analyzers. The spectra represent differential curves of dN/dE versus E
where N = number of counts having energies between E and $E + dE$; E =
energy of radiation.

Detailed information on pulse height analyzers has been compiled by a numbe
of workers.[30-33]

REFERENCES

1. G. B. COOK and J. F. DUNCAN, *Modern Radiochemical Practice.* Oxfor
   University Press, Oxford (1952).
2. E. BLEULER and G. J. GOLDSMITH, *Experimental Nucleonics*, Rinehart, Ne
   York (1952).
3. D. TAYLOR, *The Measurement of Radio Isotopes*, Wiley, New York (1951)
4. C. E. CROUTHAMEL, (Ed.), *Applied Gamma-Ray Spectrometry*, Pergamo
   Press, The Macmillan Company, New York (1960).
5. L. SALMON, U.K. A.E.R.E. Report No. AERE-C/R-2377(1) (1959).
6. R. L. Heath, U.S. Atomic Energy Comm. Rept. IDO-16408 (1957).
7. T. SCHNEIDER and H. MUENZEL, *Atompraxis*, **7**, 1 (1961).
8. H. I. WEST, Jr. and B. JOHNSTON, *I.R.E. Trans. Nucl. Sci.*, **NS-7**, 111 (1960)
9. L. J. BEAUFAIT, Jr., E. E. ANDERSON and J. P. PETERSON, *Anal. Chem.*, **30**
   1762 (1958).
10. W. B. MANN and H. H. SELIGER, U.S. National Bureau of Standards
    Washington, Cir. 594 (1958).
11. N. RADIN, (Ed.), U.S. Atomic Energy Comm. Rept. TID-6374 (1960).
12. A. C. KUYPER, *J. Chem. Ed.*, **36**, 128 (1959).
13. L. J. RAINWATER and C. W. WU, *Nucleonics*, **1**, No. 2, 60 (1947).
14. A. A. JARRETT, U.S. Atomic Energy Comml Rept. AECU-262 (1946).
15. Tech. Bull. No. 14, Nuclear-Chicago Corp., Des Plaines, Ill. (1962).
16. A. J. MOSES, *Analytical Chemistry of the Actinide Elements*, Pergamon Press
    The Macmillan Company, New York (1963).
17. G. FRIEDLANDER and J. W. KENNEDY, *Nuclear and Radiochemistry*, Wiley
    New York (1955).
18. R. T. OVERMAN and H. M. CLARK, *Radioisotope Techniques*, McGraw–Hil
    New York (1960).
19. National Academy of Sciences-National Research Council, Nuclear Scienc
    Series: see Appendix B.
20. J. S. HANDLOSER, *Health Physics Instrumentation*, Pergamon Press, Ne
    York (1959).
21. W. T. DABBS and F. J. WALTER, (Eds.), *Semiconductor Nuclear Particl
    Detectors*, National Academy of Sciences, National Research Counci
    Washington, Publ. No. 871 (1961).
22. W. L. BROWN, *I.R.E. Trans. on Nucl. Sci.*, **NS-8**, No. 1, 2 (1961).
23. G. D. O'KELLEY, National Academy of Sciences-National Research Counci
    Nuclear Science Series, Rept. NAS-NS-3105 (1962).
24. G. L. MILLER, W. M. GIBSON and P. F. DONOVAN, *Ann. Rev. Nucl. Sci.*, **12**
    189 (1962).

. L. F. CURTISS, U.S. National Bureau of Standards, Cir. 490 (1950).
. H. FRIEDMAN, *Proc. I.R.E.*, **37**, 791 (1949).
. C. G. BELL and F. N. HAYES, (Eds.), *Liquid Scintillation Counting*, Pergamon Press, New York (1958).
. H. YAGODA, *Radioactive Measurements with Nuclear Emulsions*, Wiley, New York (1949).
. W. P. NORRIS and L. A. WOODRUFF, *Ann. Rev. Nucl. Sci.*, **5**, 297 (1955).
. A. B. VAN RENNES, *Nucleonics*, **10**, No. 7, 20; No. 8, 22; No. 9, 32; No. 10, 50 (1952).
. G. G. KELLEY, Proc. First Int. Conf. on Peaceful Uses of Atomic Energy, Geneva, Vol. 14 (1955).
. W. A. HIGINBOTHAM, *I.R.E. Trans. Nucl. Sci.*, **NS-3**, No. 4, 3 (1956).
. V. O. VYAZEMSKIĬ, I. I. LOMONOSOV, A. N. PISAREVSKIĬ, Kh. V. PROTOPOPOV, V. A. RUZIN and E. D. TETERIN, U. S. Atomic Energy Comm. Rep. AEC-TR-5259 (1961); translation from Russian.

CHAPTER 3

MEASUREMENT OF NATURAL RADIOACTIVITY

A NUMBER of naturally occurring isotopes are radioactive. The include members of the U^{235}, U^{238} and the Th^{232} series as well certain isotopes of potassium, rubidium, lanthanum, lutetiur samarium, rhenium and possibly a few others. Table 3.1 offe information on some naturally occurring radio-isotopes found the earth's crust.

TABLE 3.1. NATURALLY OCCURRING RADIOISOTOPES

Isotope	Half-life, years	Isotopic abundance, %	Specific α or β activity, dpm g⁻ of element
K^{40}	1.39×10^9	0.019	1.75×10^3 β
Rb^{87}	4.7×10^{10}	27.8	5.5×10^4 β
La^{138}	1.2×10^{11}	0.089	1.6×10^1 β
Sm^{147}	1.3×10^{11}	15.1	6.1×10^3 α
Lu^{176}	2.3×10^{10}	2.60	5.1×10^3 β
Re^{187}	4.3×10^{10}	62.9	6.2×10^4 β
Th^{232}	1.39×10^{10}	100	2.5×10^5 α
U^{235}	7.13×10^8	0.7204	3.4×10^4 α
U^{238}	4.50×10^9	99.2739	7.4×10^5 α

Although counting techniques are usually considered only f• the determination of potassium, rubidium and the actinides, tl chemist working in the field of geochronology may be intereste in the analysis of other isotopes by counting techniques.

DETERMINATION OF URANIUM AND THORIUM

In view of the relative importance of counting techniques f• the determination of uranium and thorium, these elements w be discussed first. Methods for the determination of uranium and thorium by counting techniques are divided into the following two classes:

(1)   direct methods, based on measurement of particles or photons emitted by isotopes of U and Th and

(2)   indirect methods, based on measurement of other members of decay series.

Indirect methods are more frequently used, even though difficulties can arise from the possible lack of equilibrium with decay products in a series. It takes about six half-lives to achieve equilibrium with daughter products. For some chains, this period is as high as 10^6 years! Weathering of ores can lead to loss of equilibrium. It is therefore important to either use techniques that do not require equilibrium conditions or to know the degree of equilibrium.

Prospecting for uranium deposits with a Geiger–Müller counter or a scintillation counter represents a field application of the indirect measurement of uranium. The field use of these instruments has been described by Wright.[1] Equilibrium is usually assumed and the results are expressed as "uranium equivalent" after comparison with a U_3O_8 standard. Thus, a 0.26 per cent uranium equivalent ore gives off as much radioactivity as a U_3O_8 ore containing 0.26 per cent U_3O_8 in equilibrium with its decay products and free from thorium. A typical Geiger–Müller counter used for prospecting is shown in Fig. 1.3.

A more refined method by Eichholz et al.[2] permits the simultaneous measurement of thorium and uranium by measurement of beta and gamma activities with two counters. This method gives results independent of equilibrium conditions. Further details about field tests for uranium and thorium are presented in a number of excellent references.[3–5] Fig. 3.1 shows the radioactive decay chains of interest.

Owing to its selectivity, gamma spectrometry has become a powerful tool in uranium and thorium assay. The gamma spectrometry of unseparated ores is based on measurement of decay products. Figs. 3.2 and 3.3 show the gamma spectra of uranium and thorium ores in equilibrium with their decay products. The spectra were obtained by Iredale[6] with a 3in. × 3in. NaI(Tl) crystal. Uranium and thorium have been determined in the ppm range[7] by the gamma-spectrometric measurement of the 1.76 MeV

Uranium	Thorium	Radium	Radon	Polonium	Lead	
Protactinium	Actinium	Francium	Astatine	Bismuth	Thalli
92 91	90 89	88 87	86 85	84 83	82	81

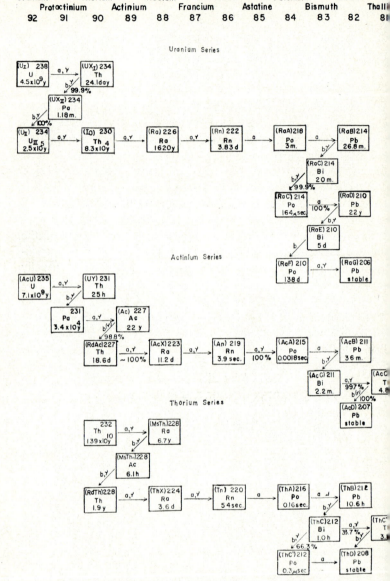

FIG. 3.1   Radioactive decay chains for uranium and thorium

After E. J. BARATTA and A. C. HERRINGTON, U.S. Atomic Energy Comm.
Rep. WIN–118, 1960

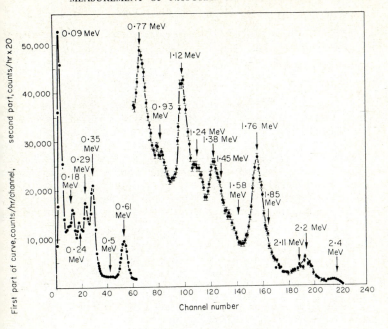

FIG. 3.2 The spectrum from uranium and its decay products
A.E.R.E. ES/R2696

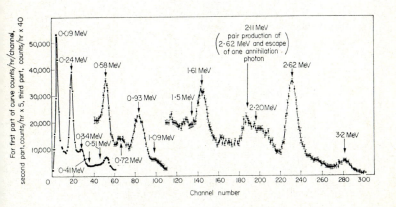

FIG. 3.3 The spectrum from thorium and its decay products
A.E.R.E. EL/R2696

4

photopeak of RaC (Bi[214]) for uranium and the 2.62 MeV peak of ThC" (Tl[208]) for thorium. Equilibrium conditions are assumed to exist between uranium and thorium and their decay products. The procedure is as follows:[7]

Procedure:
Crush the rock sample to pass a B.S.S. 100 mesh sieve and weigh 200 g into a counting can. Use only 100 g if the U or Th concentration is over 25 ppm. Prepare appropriate standards from materials, obtained from the New Brunswick Laboratory (see Appendix C) or some other, reliable source. Place the can around the 2 in.–1¾ in. NaI(Tl) crystal and count standard and sample for one hour each at the proper energies (1.76 MeV for U and 2.62 MeV for Th). Place the empty can in position to obtain background count. Calculate the U and the Th content of the sample from the following:

Let U_1 = counts from U standard at 1.76 MeV
U_2 = counts from U standard at 2.62 MeV
T_1 = counts from Th standard at 1.76 MeV
T_2 = counts from Th standard at 2.62 MeV
R_1 = counts from sample at 1.76 MeV
R_2 = counts from sample at 2.62 MeV
A_1 = counts from U in sample, at 1.76 MeV
A_2 = counts from U in sample at 2.62 MeV
B_1 = counts from Th in sample, at 1.76 MeV
B_2 = counts from Th in sample, at 2.62 MeV

Then $R_1 = A_1 + B_1$
$R_2 = A_2 + B_2$.
As $A_2/A_1 = U_2/U_1$
$B_2/B_1 = T_2/T_1$,
the following equations can be derived:

$$A_1 = \frac{\left(\dfrac{R_1 T_2}{T_1} - R_2\right)}{\left(\dfrac{T_2}{T_1} - \dfrac{U_2}{U_1}\right)}$$

$$B_1 = \frac{\left(\dfrac{R_1 U_2}{U_1} - R_2\right)}{\left(\dfrac{U_2}{U_1} - \dfrac{T_2}{T_1}\right)}$$

and

ppm U in sample = $(A_1/U_1) \times$ ppm U in standard
ppm Th in sample = $(B_1/T_1) \times$ ppm Th in standard.

Notes: 1. The sample can surrounds the crystal.
2. The use of a multichannel analyzer in place of a single channel analyzer

would result in a saving of time, owing to the simultaneous determination of counts at both gamma energies and the ability to store background data for subsequent subtraction of the background by complementing.
3.   The use of a larger crystal would further increase the sensitivity.
4.   The method is capable of analyzing levels of U or Th of 1 ppm and lower.

The direct measurement of uranium in macroamounts is possible using the 0.184 MeV gamma ray of U^{235}. This technique also serves to determine the enrichment of uranium in U^{235}. In view of the increasing demand for the determination of U^{235}, the details are presented here.[8] Although the example presented is based on the determination of uranium and U^{235} on Fiberglass filters from glove boxes, the technique is applicable to all kinds of materials.

Procedure:
Cut a fiberglass specimen, 2in. $\times$ 2in., from the filter and weigh. Treat the specimen with hot conc HNO_3, adding HCl as required, to achieve solution of dust particles. Then filter the solution, wash the filter specimen with 3 N HNO_3 and combine filtrate and wash solution. Add 25 ml of conc H_2SO_4 to the combined solution and evaporate to near dryness. Dissolve the residue in 1 N H_2SO_4 and make up to 100 ml volume. Electrolyze aliquots of the solution with a mercury cathode to remove reducible constituents such as iron, nickel and chromium. Determine the uranium content of an aliquot by titration with standard *sulfato cerate* solution, after passage of the solution (as chloride) through a lead reductor.[9,10] Take another aliquot of the electrolyzed solution, containing up to 100 mg of uranium, precipitate ammonium diuranate by addition of NH_4OH and collect the precipitate on filter paper. Dissolve the precipitate in conc HCl, evaporate to near dryness and redissolve in conc HCl. Weigh out isotopic uranium standards of approximately the same weight as the uranium content of the aliquot, and dissolve in conc HCl, containing a few drops of conc HNO_3. (Isotopic standards are listed in Appendix C. The standards should be enriched in U^{235} to such an extent that they bracket the enrichment of the sample.) Then pass the sample and standard solutions over anion exchange resin columns in the chloride form (e.g., Dowex-l) to adsorb the uranium. Wash the columns with several column lengths of 6 N HCl, then elute the uranium with 0.1 N HCl. Evaporate the eluates and ignite to U_3O_8 at 900°C. Weigh out approximately the same amount of standards and sample U_3O_8, transfer into $1\frac{1}{2}$ dram vials and dissolve the oxide in 2.0 ml of 6 N HNO_3. Place each vial into the well of the sodium iodide well crystal of the scintillation spectrometer and count under the 0.184 MeV photo-

peak from U^{235}. Calculate the U^{235} content of the sample by comparison with data from the standards and a knowledge of the uranium content of sample and standards.

Notes: 1. Ion exchange separation removes the uranium decay products, shown in Fig. 3.1.
2. Single or multichannel analyzers may be used. Multichannel analyzers permit attainment of greater accuracy, owing to their ability to simulate the enrichment of samples, rather than relying on interpolation.

Based on the measurement of the 0.184 MeV photopeak of U^{235}, monitors have been devised for the continuous determination of uranium in industrial processes.[9]

DETERMINATION OF POTASSIUM

It was mentioned earlier that potassium contains naturally radioactive K^{40}, with an isotopic abundance of 0.0110 per cent. This isotope decays by a complex scheme which includes beta decay with a half life of 1.39×10^9 years, $E_{max} = 1.33$ MeV, and emission of a 1.46 MeV gamma ray. Beta counting of salts and solutions has been used by Gübeli and Stammbach[10] in the determination of potassium in salts. Belskii and Famin[11] have measured the gamma ray from K^{40} to determine the element in rocks.

DETERMINATION OF RUBIDIUM AND POTASSIUM

Rubidium contains a weak beta emitter, Rb^{87}, with an isotopic abundance of 27.8 per cent and a half-life of 4.7×10^{10} years. The beta particles have a maximum energy of 0.27 MeV. In view of the difficult separation of rubidium from potassium, the determination of rubidium in a mixture of their chlorides is of interest. Such a determination has been reported by Gübeli and Stammbach.

Procedure:
Weigh out 90 mg quantities of finely divided alkali chlorine of composition 100 per cent RbCl, 75 per cent RbCl, 50 per cent RbCl, 25 per cent RbCl, and 0 per cent RbCl, the balance in all cases being KCl. Transfer these standards into aluminum planchets having a 3 cm diameter. Place a blank aluminum planchet under a Geiger–Müller counter with 2 mg cm^{-2} mica window and take a 3 hr background count. Then, count each standard for 30 min. Insert a 0.05 mm thick aluminum absorber near the mica window and again, count all standards for 30 min. Plot a standard curve of *counting rate* versus *composition*. Prepare a similar counting

sample from material to be analyzed and count with and without 0.05 mm aluminum absorber. From these two counting rates, read the composition of the unknown from the calibration curve.

Notes: 1.   The minimum detectable concentration of rubidium was 1 per cent.
2.   Sensitivity can be greatly improved by the use of modern low-level counting devices and techniques.
3.   Although the calibration time is rather long, the method is relatively rapid where many samples need to be analyzed.

DETERMINATION OF POLONIUM

The long-lived isotope of polonium, Po^{210}, is of analytical interest. This isotope occurs in the U^{238} decay series (RaF) and can also be synthesized by neutron bombardment of bismuth. Po^{210} decays with a half life of 138.4 days by emission of 5.3 MeV alpha particles.

The chemist analyzing polonium is cautioned about the hazards of ingested polonium and is advised to use a glove box for handling amounts above 1 μc. Inasmuch as all polonium isotopes are radioactive and are analyzed at trace levels, radiochemical techniques are employed. The chemistry and the determination of polonium have been discussed in detail by Figgins.[13] Although many methods of separation of polonium are available, the spontaneous deposition or electrodeposition of the element are the simplest techniques for its separation. In spontaneous deposition, some codeposition will be encountered from bismuth; this codeposition is avoided in controlled potential electrodeposition. Erbacher[14,15] has succeeded in spontaneously depositing polonium from 1 N HCl solution and preventing deposition of bismuth by addition of thiourea.

The following method for the determination of polonium in urine is based on the spontaneous deposition of the element, as reported by Milligan,[16]

Procedure:
Measure 100 ml of urine and transfer into a 150 ml beaker, rinse the measuring volume with 20 ml of 6 N HCl and combine rinse with sample. Place sample in a constant temperature bath, held at 50–55°C. Degrease a nickel disc with trichloroethylene, nitric acid, water, HCl and, finally water. Then suspend the

nickel disc on a glass hook in the sample solution and stir the solution for one hour with an electrically-driven stirrer. Remove the disc, wash with water, and air-dry. Count the alpha activity on each side of the disc with a windowless proportional flow counter for 30 min. Determine the background of the counter, using a properly cleaned blank nickel disc. Add the counts from both sides of the sample, substract the background, and report polonium as dpm/l. of urine.

Note. Counting efficiency is approximately 51 per cent.

DETERMINATION OF RADIUM

The following method for the determination of radium is by Kahn and Goldin[17] and is based on the complexing of barium–radium sulfate with EDTA.

Procedure:

Add the following reagents in the order shown to one liter of aqueous sample solution: 5 ml of 1 M citric acid solution, containing 0.1 per cent phenol; 2.5 ml of conc NH_4OH; 2 ml of 1 N $Pb(NO_3)_2$ solution; 1.00 ml of 0.100 N $Ba(NO_3)_2$ solution. Then heat the solution to boiling, add 10 drops of 0.1 per cent methyl orange, add with stirring sufficient conc H_2SO_4 to a pink color and 0.25 ml in excess. Digest for 10 min, let settle for 1–2 hr, decant, and discard the supernate. Transfer the precipitate into a 50-ml centrifuge tube, using two portions of conc HNO_3 to achieve the transfer and wash the precipitate, centrifuge and discard the supernate. Dissolve the precipitate in a mixture of 10 ml of H_2O, 10 ml of 0.25 M EDTA (disodium salt) and 3ml of 6 N NH_4OH. Warm the solution, add dropwise 2 ml of glacial acetic acid, digest for 10 min, centrifuge and discard the supernate. Note the time (see Note 1). Wash the reprecipitated $BaSO_4$ with water and transfer to a counting planchet. Dry, flame, weigh and count the alpha activity. Calculate the Ra^{226} activity from counting data and from the growth of daughter activity.

Notes: 1.   From this separation on, radon and daughters grow into the $BaSO_4$ precipitate.
2.   Isotopic or chemical purity of Ra^{226} can be established by recounting the precipitate after 24–48 hr. Growth of the daughters from Ra^{226}, assuming the absence of Ra^{223}, is indicated in Table 3.2.
3.   Recovery of 80–85 per cent has been reported by the authors[17] at a level of 2 dpm of Ra per liter.

TABLE 3.2. GROWTH OF DAUGHTER PRODUCTS FROM Ra^{226}[18]

Time from separation	Alpha activity/initial alpha activity (at 100% counting efficiency)
0 hr	1.0000
4 hr	1.0798
8 hr	1.1668
12 hr	1.2511
18 hr	1.3729
1 day	1.4892
2 days	1.9034
3 days	2.2525
4 days	2.5422
5 days	2.7838
6 days	2.9853
7 days	3.1536
8 days	3.2939
9 days	3.4110
10 days	3.5086

DETERMINATION OF PROTACTINIUM

A relatively simple procedure for the determination of protactinium in urine has been developed by Russell[19]

Procedure:
Transfer 400 ml of urine to a beaker, rinse the container with 100 ml of conc HNO_3 and combine rinse with sample. Evaporate to dryness and ash to a white solid with the aid of alternate treatments with conc HNO_3 and H_2O_2. Add 50 ml of conc HCl to the residue and evaporate to near dryness at low heat. Add 60 ml of 10 M HCl to the residue and heat 15 min with occasional stirring. Decant the hot solution into a 125 ml separatory funnel, wash the residue with 20 ml of hot 10 M HCl and decant into the same separatory funnel. Add 25 ml of di-isopropyl ketone to the hot solution and shake the separatory funnel for 10 min. Discard the aqueous layer and transfer the ketone to a beaker. Rinse the funnel with 5 ml of ketone and combine the rinse with the main ketone fraction. Evaporate the ketone to dryness in a drying oven at 100–110°C, then ignite in a muffle furnace at 250–300°C for 10 min. Let the beaker cool, then dissolve the residue in warm conc HNO_3 and evaporate aliquots on counting planchets and count the appropriate protactinium activity.

Notes: 1. The average recovery in eight samples was 84 ± 6 per cent, as reported by Russell.[19]

2.   The tendency of Pa to form colloidal hydrous oxides may give irreproducible results.

3.   The method may be used to determine any Pa isotope. Pa^{233} may be counted by measuring the 0.10 or 0.31 MeV photopeaks or by alpha counting and Pa^{231} by alpha counting. The 27 keV gamma peak of Pa^{231} is useful for identification as both its 95 and 300 keV photopeaks are similar to the spectrum of Pa^{233}.

DETERMINATION OF ACTINIUM

Actinium analyses, like protactinium, are usually determined on a trace scale. Owing to its similarity with lanthanides, actinium is usually coprecipitated with lanthanum fluoride, oxalate, carbonate or hydroxide. The following procedure by Iddings[20] is a relatively rapid analysis.

Procedure:

Add about 5 mg of pure lutetium carrier to the sample solution. Precipitate the $Lu(OH)_3$ by the addition of NaOH to a pH over 13. Wash the precipitate with water and dissolve in 5 ml of buffer solution, pH 5.7 (0.1 M acetic acid and 1 M sodium acetate). Extract the Ac and Lu into 30 ml of 0.40 M TTA in benzene, stirring the phases for at least 3 min. Wash the organic layer twice with 15 ml of buffer solution. Back-extract Ac (not the Lu) into 10 ml of pH 4.5 buffer solution (0.1 M formic acid and 1 M sodium formate). Repeat back-extraction with another 10 ml portion of pH 4.5 buffer solution. Combine the aqueous solutions. Extract the Ac into a new 30 ml volume of 0.40 M TTA in benzene. Wash the organic phase with 15 ml of pH 5.7 buffer solution and discard the wash solution. Back-extract the Ac into 5 ml of 0.05 M HCl. Repeat back-extraction with a second 5 ml volume of 0.05 M HCl. Combine the aqueous extracts, and evaporate to a small volume, finally transferring the extract to a platinum disc for further evaporation and ignition over a Meeker burner. Count the Ac activity.

Notes: The weak beta activity from Ac^{227} is usually counted in a windowless gas flow proportional counter. Ac^{228} is detected by beta counting with a proportional or Geiger–Müller counter. When Ac^{227} and Ac^{228} are both present, Ac^{227} beta activity can be shielded with absorbers[21]

REFERENCES

1. R. J. WRIGHT, *Prospecting with a Counter*, U.S. Atomic Energy Comm., Washington (1954).
2. G. G. EICHHOLZ, J. W. HILBORN and C. MCMAHON, *Can. J. Phys.*, **31**, 613 (1953).

3. A. A. SMALES and L. R. WAGER (Eds.), *Methods in Geochemistry*, Interscience Publishers, New York (1960).

4. H. FAUL (Ed.), *Nuclear Geology*, Wiley, New York (1954).

5. V. L. SHASKIN, *Methods of Analysis of Natural Radioelements*, State Publishing House of Literature on Atomic Science and Technology, Moscow (1961); U.S. Atomic Energy Comm. Translation No. AEC-tr-5458.

6. P. IREDALE, U.K. Atomic Energy Research Establ. Rept. AERE-EL/R-2696, (1958).

7. T. W. BLOXAM, *J. Sci. Instr.*, **39**, 387 (1962).

8. A. J. MOSES, T. B. CROCKETT and J. T. GREEN, *Determination of Total Uranium and Uranium-235 on Spun Fiberglass Filters*, Paper No. 72, Pittsburgh Conf. on Analytical Chemistry and Applied Spectroscopy, March (1963).

9. M. R. HAYES and A. P. SEYFANG, *Talanta*, **9**, 517 (1962).

10. O. GÜBELI and K. STAMMBACH, *Helv. Chim. Acta*, **34**, 1245 (1951).

11. V. E. BELSKII and O. K. FAMIN, *Zavodskyya Lab.*, **26**, 707 (1960).

12. O. GÜBELI and K. STAMMBACH, *Helv. Chim. Acta*, **34**, 1253 (1951).

13. P. E. FIGGINS, National Academy of Sciences-National Research Council, Nuclear Science Series, Rep. NAS-NS-3037 (1961).

14. O. ERBACHER, *Naturwiss.*, **20**, 390 (1932).

15. O. ERBACHER, *Z. Elektrochem*, **38**, 532 (1932).

16. M. F. MILLIGAN, E. E. CAMPBELL, B. C. EUTSLER, J. McCLELLAND and W. D. MOSS, U.S. Atomic Energy Comm. Rep. LA-1858, 2nd ed. (1958).

17. B. KAHN and A. S. GOLDIN, *J. Am. Waterworks Assocn.*, **49**, 767 (1957).

18. H. W. KIRBY, U.S. Atomic Energy Comm. Rep. MLM-859 (1953).

19. E. R. RUSSELL, U.S. Atomic Energy Comm. Rep. AECD-2516 (1958).

20. IDDINGS, reported in: P. C. STEVENSON and W. E. NERVIK, National Academy of Sciences-National—Research Council, Nuclear Sciences Series, Rep. NAS-NS-3020 (1961).

21. E. J. BARATTA and M. H. FELDMAN, U.S. Atomic Energy Comm. Rep. WIN-123 (1961).

CHAPTER 4

PRINCIPLES OF ACTIVATION ANALYSIS

IN order to meet the demand for the determination of impuritie
at the ppm and ppb level, the analytical chemist has turned wit
increasing frequency to activation analysis. This technique is base
on induced radioactivity and subsequent characterization of thi
activity.

The desirable features of activation analysis are:

(1) the rapidity of analysis,

(2) the insensitivity to chemical form of element,

(3) the non-destructive nature of analysis,

(4) the high sensitivity if a large particle flux is available,

(5) the availability of a signal for automatic recording of result
and automatic control of a process, and

(6) the equipment requirements may be relatively inexpensive

Owing to the relatively high probability of forming radio
nuclides upon irradiation with neutrons, this type of activatio
has by far become the most widely used activation technique
Although emphasis in this chapter is placed on neutron activatior
much of the information is equally applicable to activatio
with charged particles and photons.

Activation analysis requires a consideration of the laws goverr
ing growth and decay in radioactivation. The following abbrevia
tions will be used:

f = activating flux, in particles $cm^{-2} sec^{-1}$
N = number of target nuclei of isotope
T = half-life of radioactive product
λ = decay constant of radioactive product = $0.693/T$
N_t = number of radioactive atoms produced after activation for time t
σ = activation cross section of reaction, in cm^2

The rate of growth of the activity is expressed by

$$dN/dt = Nf\sigma = \lambda N \qquad (1$$

nd integration between the limits $t = 0$ and $t = t$ yields:

$$N_t = \frac{Nf\sigma}{\lambda} (1 - e^{-\lambda t}) \qquad (2)$$

Because the activity is defined as $A_t = \lambda N_t$, $\qquad (3)$
he above equations can be rewritten as:

$$A_t = \lambda N_t = Nf\sigma (1 - e^{-\lambda t}). \qquad (4)$$

$Nf\sigma$ is called "saturation activity $(A\infty)$" and the term $(1 = e^{-\lambda t})$ is
requently called "saturation factor." It should be noted that
rradiation for *one* half-life produces 50 per cent saturation, while
rradiation for *four* half-lives gives only 94 per cent saturation.

The saturation factor is plotted as a function of time in Fig. 4.1.
Obviously, it is generally not worthwhile to irradiate a sample for
 period exceeding five or six half-lives. Where $t < 0.15$ T, an
rror of less than 5 per cent is introduced by simplifying equation
4) as

$$A_t = A\infty \lambda t. \qquad (5)$$

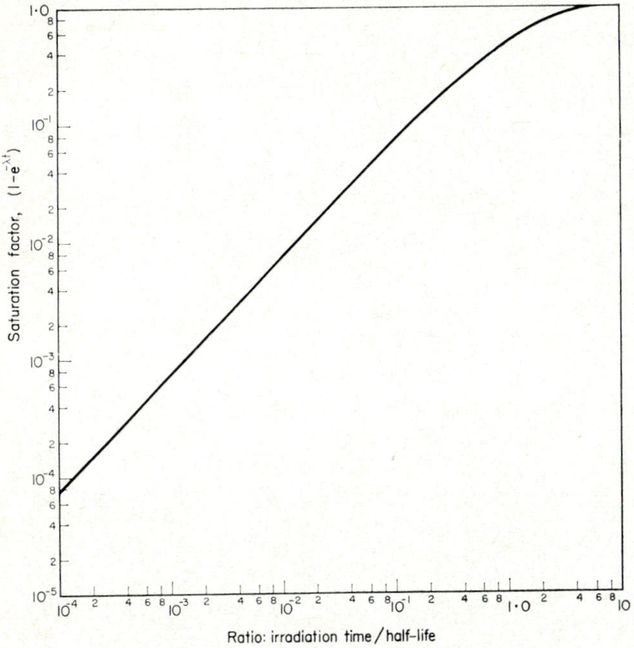

FIG. 4.1   Saturation factor versus irradiation time

By inserting Avogadro's number, the weight of the desired element (W), the isotopic abundance (I) and the atomic weight (M) in equation (4), the latter can be written as:

$$A_t = \frac{W \times I \times 6.02 \times 10^{23}}{M} f\sigma (1 - e^{-\lambda t}) \qquad (6$$

The decay of activity A_t must also be taken into account. The decay obeys the relationship

$$A_t' = A_t \, e^{-\lambda t'} \qquad (7$$

where t' denotes the time interval between the end of the irradiation and the time of measurement. Fig. 4.2 shows the relationship

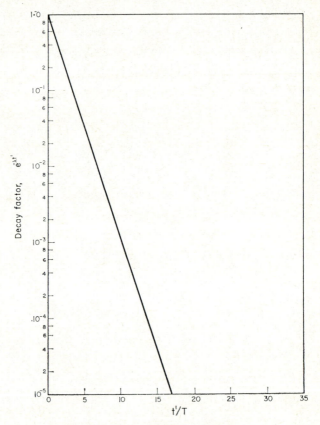

FIG. 4.2   Decay factor versus decay time

etween the "decay factor," $e^{-\lambda t'}$ and the ratio t'/T. As will be hown later, decay during the sample transfer can be a significant actor in activation analysis.

ample Calculations:

What is the activity induced in 1 μg of osmium by the reaction Os^{192} (n, γ) Os^{193} fter one hour's irradiation in a thermal neutron flux of 1×10^{12} n cm^{-2} sec^{-1}? Vhat will the activity be if the sample cannot be counted until 6 days after the nd of the irradiation?

The numbers to be inserted in equation (6) are:

$W = 1 \times 10^{-6}$ g
$I = 0.41$ (41 per cent)
$M = 190$
$f = 1 \times 10^{12}$ n cm^{-2} sec^{-1}
$\sigma = 1.6 \times 10^{-24}$ cm^2 (1.6 barns)
$T_{\frac{1}{2}} = 1.33$ days or 1.15×10^5 sec
$t = 1$ hr

Thus, from equation (6):

$A_t = 2.08 \times 10^3 (1 - e^{-\lambda t})$ dps

here 2.08×10^3 dps represents the saturation activity, A_∞ (Appendix D gives ,2 $\times 10^5$ dpm, corresponding to 2.0×10^3 dps.)

Equation (5) permits a simplification in calculating the saturation factor, i.e.,

$$\lambda t = \frac{0.693}{1.15 \times 10^5} \times 3.6 \times 10^3 = 2.2 \times 10^{-2}$$

Thus the solution to the first part of the problem is $1.2 \times 10^5 \times 2.2 \times 10^{-2}$ $= 2.6 \times 10^3$ dpm. (Appendix D gives 2.8×10^3 dpm at the end of the irradiation.) In the second part of the problem, the decay period is $6.0/1.33 = 4.5$ half-lives. igure 4.2 gives a corresponding decay factor of 4.6×10^{-2}. Therefore the ctivity after 6 days is $4.6 \times 10^{-2} \times 1.2 \times 10^5 = 5.5 \times 10^3$ dpm.

Neutron capture with release of a gamma ray has a relatively igh probability for slow neutrons. This probability is frequently iversely proportional to the velocity of the neutrons. Neutrons /ith the most probable velocity of 2.2×10^5 cm sec^{-1} in a Max-/ellian distribution at 20°C (0.025 eV in energy) are called "thermal eutrons." Thermal neutrons are obtained by exposing fast eutrons to moderating materials such as water and paraffin. `able 2.5 lists thermal and fast neutron fluxes of some of the more ommonly encountered sources of neutrons, Appendix D provides nformation for (n, γ) reactions of analytical interest. The informa- on in Appendix D includes half-life of product, isotopic abund- nce of parent, activation cross section, beta and gamma ray data, s well as the specific activity resulting from irradiation to satura- on and for 1 hr, using a thermal flux of 10^{12} n cm^{-2} sec^{-1}.

At times, selective activation by resonance neutrons can be achieved by the use of filters such as cadmium and boron thus resulting in appreciable enhancement of one activity over others An example of the use of resonance neutrons will be given subse quently in connection with the determination of manganese in biological materials.

Many of the lighter elements have low (n, γ) activation cros sections and short-lived activation products, whereas the cros section for fast neutron activations, i.e., (n, p), (n, α) and (n, 2n are relatively high for the light elements. Fast neutron activation frequently require neutrons with energies near 14 MeV. Such neutrons are not readily available in copious amounts in many reactors, but are produced in good yield in van de Graaff and Cockroft–Walton accelerators. Table 2.5 includes data on accelera tors. Use of moderating materials such as water or paraffin around the target assembly extends the usefulness of accelerators to thermal neutron activations. Figs. 2.6 and 2.7 show a neutron generator and its installation for fast neutron activation. Fig. 4.3 lists elements that can be determined with sensitivities of 10 ppm or better, following five minute fast neutron irradiation of one gram samples. Similar information with sensitivities of 100 ppm is provided for thermal neutrons in Fig. 4.4; both figures are based on an activating flux of 1×10^9 n cm^{-2} sec^{-1} and a disintegration rate of 100 dpm. More detailed information on neutron activation is presented in tabular form in Appendices D and E.

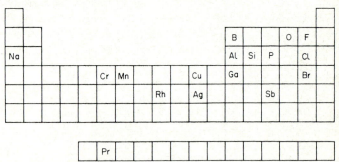

FIG. 4.3   Sensitivity for fast neutron reactions*

*Limit of detection taken as 10 ppm, based on 5 min irradiation with 14 MeV neutrons of flux 1×10^9 n/cm²/sec and minimum disintegration rate of 100 dpm

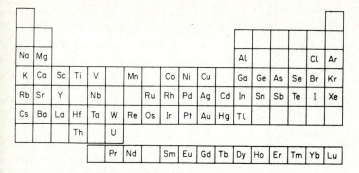

FIG. 4.4 Sensitivity for thermal neutron reactions*

Owing to a lack of accurate information concerning the flux spectrum and activation cross sections, the chemist will frequently irradiate a comparison standard simultaneously with the sample material. Considerable emphasis is placed on the comparator method in this text.

Other neutrons activation techniques include the irradiation of fissionable material with subsequent counting of delayed neutrons and the neutron irradiation of lithium to form tritons that subsequently react with nuclei.

Briefly, activation analysis involves the following steps:

(1) Investigation of the feasibility of the technique using data in Appendices D and E, considering:
   (a) type of activation, sensitivity of technique, and interfering reactions,
   (b) availability of activating source and radiation measuring devices,
   (c) cost of activation technique versus cost by non-nuclear techniques.

(2) Sample preparation
   (a) choose suitable containers and load them with aliquots of sample and comparator. Aluminum, quartz, polyethylene, and polystyrene are commonly used containers; keep in mind irradiation temperature, chemical inertness of container, etc.

*Limit of detection taken as 100 ppm, based on one hour irradiation with thermal neutrons of flux 1×10^9 n/cm²/sec and minimum disintegration rate of 100 dpm.

(3) Irradiation
  (a) Irradiate samples and comparators in as nearly the same flux as possible.

(4) Purification
  (a) if analysis by direct γ-spectrometry is possible, transfer materials to unirradiated counting containers.
  (b) if necessary, dissolve materials, add inactive carrier and purify using radiochemical techniques.

(5) Comparative measurement
  (a) Intensities of radiation from samples and comparator are determined and corrections made for decay, chemical yield, counting efficiency, self-shielding during irradiation, and correlated with the weight of element in the materials.

Errors in thermal neutron activation analysis have been discussed in detail [1-3] and suggest attention to the following factors

(1) fast neutron reactions,
(2) fission products from fission of uranium,
(3) radioactive daughters of primary radionuclides,
(4) radionuclides with high activation cross section,
(5) inhomogeneity in flux,
(6) self-shielding and attenuation of flux by resonance effect
(7) sample preparation and chemical operations and
(8) activity measurement.

In general an understanding of these factors is vital to the performance of accurate neutron activation analyses. These factors will now be discussed.

FAST NEUTRON REACTIONS

The ratio of thermal to fast neutrons in a reactor changes with position of the specimens in the reactor. Thus the interference from (n, p), (n, α) and (n, 2n) reactions will vary with specimen location in the reactor. Knowledge of the flux distribution in a reactor or other source of neutrons is frequently obtained by irradiation of foils, both with and without cadmium covers and subsequent counting of the induced activity. The use of 0.01 in. of cadmium around foils suffices to prevent transmission of neutrons below 0.4 eV in energy. One (n, α) reaction has its highest cross section for thermal neutrons, i.e., B^{10} (n, α) Li^7; however, this is an exceptional case.

In some cases, the deliberate use of (n, p) reactions in place of n, γ) reactions is advisable owing to ease of detection of the nduced activity, longer half-life or greater freedom from interfering reactions. Examples include: Ti^{48} (n, p) Sc^{48}, Ni^{58} (n, p) Co^{58}, ^{32} (n, p) P^{32}, P^{31} (n, p) Si^{31} and Cl^{35} (n, p) S^{35}. As suggested earlier, it is advisable to review thermal and fast neutron activation nformation for all elements, expected in a specimen, before making decision on the type of activation.

FISSION PRODUCTS FROM THE FISSION OF URANIUM

Most fission products are not identical to (n, γ) activation products. Exceptions are Zr^{95}, Ru^{103}, Ru^{105}, $Nd^{147,149}$, Mo^{99}, and daughter products Te^{99m}, Nb^{95} and La^{140}.

Fission products such as Ba^{140} and Xe^{133} can be utilized to determine the amount of uranium in a specimen.

RADIOACTIVE DAUGHTERS OF PRIMARY RADIONUCLIDES

The β decay of primary radionuclides will produce the same radio nuclides of different elements as is produced in some cases by (n, γ) reactions, for example,

$$Yb^{176} \xrightarrow[n,\gamma]{} Yb^{177} \xrightarrow{\beta} Lu^{177*} \xrightarrow{\beta} Hf^{177} \text{ (stable)}$$

The review by Gebauhr[1] provides a thorough listing of such reactions.

RADIONUCLIDES WITH HIGH ACTIVATION CROSS SECTIONS

In most cases, activation of the primary product is not a significant source of error. Reactions with high "double capture" cross sections include:

$$Ta^{181} \xrightarrow[\substack{n,\gamma \\ 19 \text{ barns}}]{} Ta^{182} \xrightarrow[\substack{\beta \quad n,\gamma \\ 17,000 \text{ barns}}]{} Ta^{183} \xrightarrow{\beta} $$

$$Au^{197} \xrightarrow[\substack{n,\gamma \\ 96 \text{ barns}}]{} Au^{198} \xrightarrow[\substack{n,\gamma \\ 26,000 \text{ barns}}]{} Au^{199} \xrightarrow{\beta} $$

*Lu^{177} is also produced by the reaction: Lu^{176} (n, γ) Lu^{177}.

5

INHOMOGENEITY IN FLUX

Inhomogeneity in the unperturbed flux results in the exposure of standards and samples to different dosages with subsequent loss in accuracy. The degree of homogeneity in flux may be established by irradiation of a large foil of a monitor such as cobalt–aluminum alloy and comparing the Co^{60} beta activity induced on each side of the foil.

SELF-SHIELDING AND ATTENUATION OF FLUX BY RESONANCE EFFECTS

Attenuation of the neutron flux within the sample by neutron absorption causes a lowering of the flux toward the center of the sample. This phenomenon can introduce large errors where (n, γ) capture resonances are encountered. Fig. 4.5 shows a neutron cross section plot as a function of energy for the element iridium.

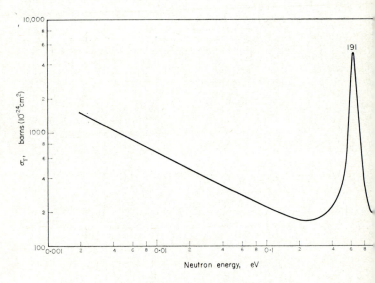

FIG. 4.5 Neutron cross section of iridium
(Redrawn from data in BNL 325)

An approximate self-shielding factor is expressed by the formula

$$f/f_0 = e^{-N\sigma x}$$

where: f_0 = incident flux, in n cm^{-2} sec^{-1}
       f = attenuated flux, in n cm^{-2} sec^{-1}
      N = number of absorber atoms cm^{-3} of material
      σ = total absorption cross section, in cm^2
      x = distance from surface of material, in cm.

Self-shielding errors are best minimized by selecting small samples and standards and using a matrix of low cross section, such as water. If the approximate concentration of the element under analysis is known, addition of aliquots of the element to specimens of the unknown is a possible approach; this technique is also known as "spiking."

SAMPLE PREPARATION AND CHEMICAL OPERATIONS

The importance of sampling and preparing samples under "sterile" conditions is well known to the analytical chemist. In view of the high sensitivity of the activation techniques, even greater care should be taken in handling samples and capsules than is the case with other analytical techniques. For example, finger prints on capsules will introduce considerable activity from traces of sodium and chlorine!

In the event, post-irradiation chemical separations are necessary, an inactive carrier of the element should be added as early as possible in the chemical procedure. The material should be completely dissolved and steps be taken to ensure isotopic exchange between radioactive and carrier species of the element. A number of reference sources are helpful in planning separations, [4-7, Appendix B]. The commonly used separation processes include precipitation, solvent extraction, ion exchange and electrodeposition. Ultimately, the chemical recovery of the element and its carrier must be established by chemical techniques such as gravimetric, volumetric, polarographic, spectrophotometric or other suitable means.

ACTIVITY MEASUREMENT

The radiochemical purity of standards and samples is established by counting under identical conditions, using beta counting, gamma spectrometry, alpha counting, or other suitable measuring technique. Half-life of nuclide, absorption characteristics and gamma spectra are aids in establishing the identity of radionuclides.

Finally, the activities of standards and samples are compared and the mass of unknown element (X) in the sample determined by calculation using the relation:

$$\frac{\text{mass of X in sample}}{\text{mass of X in standard}} = \frac{\text{Activity from X in sample}}{\text{Activity of X in standard}} \qquad (9)$$

The activities must be corrected for decay and other factors prior to their use in equation (9).

The factors involved in the measurement of radioactivity are discussed in Chapter 2. The accuracy of the activation technique is a function of errors cited above as well as counting statistics. With proper care, the technique will give results with an accuracy that is comparable to that from other tracer techniques. In many cases, a precision and accuracy of 1–2 per cent have been achieved.

REFERENCES

1. W. GEBAUHR, *Z. anal. Chem.*, **185**, 339 (1962).
2. R. C. PLUMB and J. E. LEWIS, *Nucleonics*, **13**, No. 8, 42 (1955).
3. C. E. CROUTHAMEL (Ed.), *Applied Gamma Ray Spectrometry*, Pergamon Press, Oxford (1960).
4. R. T. OVERMAN and H. M. CLARK, *Radioisotope Techniques*, McGRAW-HILL, New York (1960).
5. G. B. COOK and J. F. DUNCAN, *Modern Radiochemical Practice*, Oxford Univ. Press, Fair Lawn, N.J. (1952).
6. G. FRIEDLANDER and J. W. KENNEDY, *Nuclear and Radiochemistry*, Wiley, New York (1955).
7. E. BLEULER and G. J. GOLDSMITH, *Experimental Nucleonics*, Rinehart, New York (1952).

CHAPTER 5

NEUTRON ACTIVATION ANALYSIS

MOST elements have been determined by activation analysis using thermal or fast neutrons. In view of this fact, and the existence of a large number of papers concerning activation analysis of different elements in various matrices, this monograph offers some typical applications with the hope that they will guide the reader in applying the technique to his specific problems. Bibliographies and reviews[1-6] will prove of considerable help to the chemist preparing for activation analysis.

Direct gamma ray spectrometry on irradiated samples is the preferred counting technique owing to the speed and freedom from separations and subsequent losses of material. Various types of neutron sources are used to acquaint the reader with their application. Although a certain type of neutron source is used in a particular case, other types of sources may be equally satisfactory. Information concerning the neutron flux from various sources is given in Chapter 2. The neutron dosage depends on available flux, flux spectrum, sample size, half-life of product and desired sensitivity.

In an effort to provide information to analytical chemists working in a wide field of endeavor, examples of activation analysis have been selected from archeology, biology, chemical and metallurgical industries, criminology, crops and foods, geochemistry, petroleum industry, semi-conductors and space exploration.

ARCHEOLOGY

The non-destructive activation analysis of ancient silver coins from the fifth century B.C. has been reported by Aitken *et al.*[7] Such analyses in archeology provide information about the origin of materials and on the technology and economics of the era. In the case reported here, evidence was obtained of the debasement of coins. Following is the method employed by these authors.[7]

Procedure: Elements determined: copper, silver, gold.

Pre-irradiation treatment: place the coins weighing from 1–17 ; and the standards in irradiation can.

Irradiation: Irradiate can in the reactor with a thermal flu: to a dosage of about 3×10^{13} n, cm^{-2}.

Post-irradiation treatment: Obtain the gamma spectra of coin and standards using a gamma scintillation spectrometer. Deter mine the area under the following photopeaks:

0.511 MeV positron annihilation,   Cu^{64} 12.8 hr half-life
0.884 MeV gamma ray,   Ag^{110m} 253 day half-life
0.41 MeV gamma ray,   Au^{198} 2.69 day half-life

Make corrections for the Compton spectra from other photo peaks when determining area under peaks.

Note: The Au content ranged from 0.02 to 0.3 per cent and the Cu conten ranged from 0.1 to 10 per cent.

BIOLOGICAL MATERIALS

A number of analyses are presented involving determination: of elements in biological and plant materials.

Procedure:[8] *Element determined: Phosphorus in beetle wings.*

Pre-irradiation treatment: pack the beetle wings and the stan dards of KH_2PO in polyethylene envelopes and sandwich the envelopes between aluminum foils to reduce radiation damage to wings and envelopes. Seal the envelopes and foils into an alu minum irradiation can.

Irradiation: irradiate can for 8 hr in a thermal flux of 5×10^{12} n cm^{-2} sec^{-1}.

Post-irradiation treatment: Attach each wing with a double faced tape to a polyethylene sample holder. Prepare a similar standard by dissolving irradiated KH_2PO_4 standard material and evaporating aliquots containing 0.28 μg of P on sample holders Place the samples and standards under an end-window Geiger-Müller counter and observe decay of the activity for about one month. Monitor the stability of the counter each time with a Sr^{90}–Y^{90} source. Observe a 14-day half-life of the decay after K^{42} and Na^{24} have decayed.

Note: An average P content of 0.03 μg per wing was determined.

Procedure:[9] *Element determined: Cobalt in tissue.*

Pre-irradiation treatment: Heat-seal weighed tissue specimens into polyethylene envelopes. Then wrap gold flux-monitoring foils in polyethylene envelopes and place specimens and foils in irradia tion can.

Irradiation: Irradiate the can in thermal flux of 1×10^{12} n cm^{-2} sec^{-1} for 30 min and transfer the can to laboratory using a rapid transfer device (rabbit).

Post-irradiation treatment: Place a known amount of Co^{60} tracer and 10 mg of Co carrier solution in a nickel crucible. Add three NaOH pellets to the crucible and heat the solution to near dryness. Just prior to receipt of the irradiated specimen, add 10 g of Na$_2$O$_2$ to the crucible and melt. Add the specimen to the melt and fuse the material for one min, keeping a cover on the crucible. Then dip the crucible into a beaker of cold water to cool its contents. Dissolve the melt by the addition of 50 ml of water. Use liquid nitrogen to accelerate cooling to room temperature. Slowly add 10 ml of glacial acetic acid to the solution and cool to room temperature with liquid nitrogen. Transfer the mixture, pH of 5–6, to a 150 ml separatory funnel containing 25 ml of 8-hydroxy-quinoline solution (3 per cent in chloroform) and shake funnel for 1 min. Back the extract Co into the aqueous phase by shaking with 10 ml of 9 M HCl. Add Na$_2$O$_2$ to the HCl solution to precipitate the oxide. Then collect the precipitate on a filter chimney, wash with water, and place the prepared counting specimen in the gamma ray spectrometer. Obtain spectra, at 0–0.25 and 0–2 MeV, and determine the area under the 0.059 MeV peak (Co^{60m}). Use the 1.17 and 1.33 MeV peaks of the added Co^{60} to determine the chemical yield. Correct the Co^{60m} data for the chemical yield. Count the 0.411 MeV photopeak from the gold foils on the gamma spectrometer to determine the neutron dosage and normalize the cobalt data to a flux of 1×10^{12} n cm^{-2} sec^{-1} (standard Co activations were run previously). Calculate the cobalt content of the specimens.

Note: After irradiation in a thermal flux of 1×10^{12} n cm^{-2} sec^{-1} and a 15 min radiochemical separation with 40 per cent chemical yield, a lower limit of 5×10^{-8} g of cobalt was obtained.

Procedure:[10] *Element determined: Molybdenum in plant material*
Pre-irradiation treatment: Place a sample of about 0.5 g of clover and a 4 μg Mo standard (in quartz) in a Plexiglass can.

Irradiation: Irradiate can for 20 min at a thermal flux of 1.4×10^{12} n cm^{-2} sec^{-1} for Mo^{101}, or for 5 hr in the same flux for Mo^{99}.

Post-irradiation treatment: Let the sample cool for 20 hr if Mo^{99} is to be determined; otherwise, start immediately with sample dissolution. Add 15 mg of MoO$_3$ carrier to the sample, then 4 ml of conc H$_2$SO$_4$ and heat to fumes of SO$_3$. Destroy all the organic matter by the dropwise addition of 5 ml of an oxidizing solution, containing 2.5 ml of 70 per cent HClO$_4$ and 2.5 ml of conc HNO$_3$. Boil the solution to expel the excess acids. Cool the solution and carefully add 20 ml of water. Neutralize with 4 N

NaOH solution and filter through glass wool. Extract the solution with 25.0 ml of TOA solution (2.5 V/V per cent solution of tri-N-octylamine in petroleum ether), allow the phases to separate and pipet 20.0 ml of the organic layer. Dissolve the standard in 25.0 ml of 2 N NaOH solution and pipet 20.0 ml of this solution. Analyze the solutions by placing them in bottles in the well of a 3in. × 3in. NaI (Tl) crystal and obtain the gamma spectra. Mo^{101} is analyzed by its 0.191 MeV peak, Mo^{99} by its 0.140 MeV peak.

Note: The Mo content of clover was determined as 1 ppm. The time for the complete analysis, including 20 min irradiation, was 75 min.

Procedure:[11] *Element determined: Gold in biological materials.*

Pre-irradiation treatment: Seal 1–g samples of tissue into polyethylene bags. Seal a standard gold chloride solution into a quartz ampoule. Place the samples and standard in an irradiation can.

Irradiation: Irradiate the can in a thermal flux of 1×10^{12} n cm^{-2} sec^{-1} for a period, depending on the desired sensitivity.

Post-irradiation treatment: Transfer the irradiated sample into a 250 ml beaker, add gold carrier solution containing 30 mg of Au as chloride and add the following reagents: 2 ml of H_2O_2, 5 ml of conc H_2SO_4, 5 ml of conc HNO_3 and 2 ml of 70 per cent $HClO_4$. Cover the beaker and heat to white fumes. Add 20 ml of aqua regia, evaporate to near dryness and take up the residue in a mixture of 1 ml of conc HCl and 20 ml of water. Add 10 mg of NaCl and 10 mg of ammonium phosphate holdback carriers and a slight excess of magnesium powder to precipitate the gold. Boil the solution to expel hydrogen, cool and centrifuge. Decant the supernate and wash the precipitate with hot water. Dissolve the gold in a few drops of aqua regia and dilute with 10 ml of water and mixed holdback carriers. Add 2 ml of conc HCl, heat almost to boiling and precipitate gold by addition of 0.5 g of hydroquinone. Transfer the precipitate onto a Hirsch funnel and wash the precipitate twice with 10 ml portions of water and ethanol. Finally, dry to constant weight. Obtain the gamma spectrum and integrate the 0.411 MeV photopeak from Au^{198}. Correct the counting data for chemical yield. Open the irradiated gold standard solution and wash the ampoule out with gold carrier solution. Precipitate the gold with hydroquinone and prepare counting sample, as stated earlier. Compare the standard and sample counting data, correct for chemical yield, and calculate the gold content of sample.

Note: As little as 10^{-10} g of Au can be determined with an accuracy of 5–10 per cent.

Procedure:[12] *Element determined: Arsenic in marine organisms.*

Pre-irradiation treatment: Seal 500 mg of ashed material in

quartz tubing. Seal the sample and standard flux monitoring foil (Al–Co alloy) in polyethylene container.

Irradiation: Irradiate the container for 5–9 hr in a thermal flux of 1×10^{12} n cm^{-2} sec^{-1}.

Post-irradiation treatment: After a 15 hr cooling period, dissolve the samples in 5 ml of hot conc HNO$_3$. Add 10 mg of P carrier as phosphate and dilute to 50 ml with water. Add 1 ml of bromine water to oxidize As^{+3} to As^{+5} and boil to expel excess bromine. Then add to the hot solution 3 g of NH$_4$NO$_3$ crystals and 10 ml of 10 per cent ammonium molybdate solution. Let the solution stand for 20 min, filter off the precipitated phosphomolybdate, dry, and mount for counting. Count the 0.56 MeV photopeak from As^{76} and correct the data for chemical yield, using a factor obtained from previous As^{76} tracer runs (typical yield~60 per cent). Arsenic is coprecipitated on phosphomolybdate). Determine the induced Co^{60} activity in the monitor foil and normalize the arsenic data to a condition of a 5 hr irradiation at a thermal flux of 1×10^{12} n cm^{-2} sec^{-1}. Calculate the As content of the samples.

Note: A lower limit of detection of 0.1 μg of As was established under the experimental conditions.

Procedure:[13] Element determined: Manganese in biological material.

Manganese can be determined by selective activation of the element with a filtered reactor neutron spectrum and triple coincidence spectrometry. Owing to the relative complexity of the technique, only the principles are outlined here. The reader is urged to consult the original literature[13] for details. The resonance activation of Mn in ashed biological material is enhanced relative to elements such as Cl and Na by filling the hollow walls of the aluminum irradiation can with boron powder, enriched to 93 per cent B^{10}. This filter acts to absorb neutrons below approximately 100 eV in energy. A gain in the Mn/Na detection ratio of 6.5 is achieved, compared to that obtained with unfiltered flux. Use of triple coincidence spectrometry, involving measurement of beta and gamma radiation, eliminates the need for a radiochemical separation. Although this technique requires considerable effort initially, the chemist may find it useful where many, similar analyses must be performed.

CHEMICAL AND METALLURGICAL INDUSTRIES

Activation analysis has found wide application in the chemical and metallurgical industries.

Procedure:[14] Elements determined: Bromine and iodine in organic halogen compounds.

Pre-irradiation treatment: Dissolve 0.5 to 1 g of the material in an appropriate solvent such as water, benzene or methyl alcohol and adjust the volume to 5.00 ml. Transfer the solution into a polyethylene capsule, 86 mm length × 16 mm diameter × 1 mm wall thickness.

Irradiation: Irradiate the capsule in a neutron howitzer containing typically a 50 mg Ra–Be source (see Fig. 5.1) for one hour.

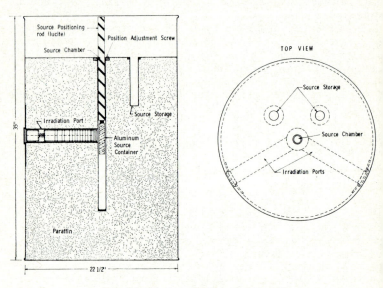

FIG. 5.1   Neutron howitzer (schematic)

Post-irradiation treatment: Allow 2.5 min for the sample transfer, then measure the induced activities on a well-type gamma scintillation spectometer. The induced activities are shown in Table 5.1.

TABLE 5.1. INDUCED BROMINE AND IODINE ACTIVITIES

Radionuclide	Half-life	Photon energies, MeV
Br^{80}	18 min	0.51, 0.62
Br^{80m}	4.58 hr	0.037, 0.049
Br^{82}	1.50 days	0.55, 0.77, 1.03
I^{128}	25.0 min	0.47, 0.54, 0.99

Determine the Br and I contents of the samples by comparison with irradiated standard samples.

Note: Br and I were analyzed to an accuracy of 4 per cent or better with improvement possible by the use of a higher neutron flux.

Procedure:[15] *Elements determined: Sc, Cr, Fe, Co, Zn, Rb, Ag, Cd, Sn, Cs, Hf, Th, and U in aluminum.*

Owing to the complexity of this analysis for 13 elements, a flow sheet of the authors' chemical separations is reproduced here as Fig. 5.2. The scheme of analysis illustrates how various chemical separation techniques are combined to provide an efficient, overall system for the analysis of many elements in one specimen using one irradiation. Gamma spectrometry is used for all measurements.

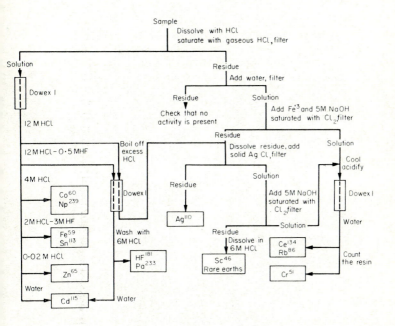

Fig. 5.2 Separation scheme for the determination of long-lived gamma-emitting impurities in reactor grade aluminum

Procedure:[16] *Element determined: Gallium in aluminum.*

Pre-irradiation treatment: Weigh out 20–30 mg of Al as well as suitable Ga standards and seal into polyethylene vials.

Irradiation: Irradiate the materials for 30–40 min in a thermal flux of 10^{12} n cm^{-2} sec^{-1}.

Post-irradiation treatment: Allow at least 17 hr for the 2.58 hr

Mn^{56} to decay, then determine the Ga by measuring the 0.83 MeV photopeak from 14.3 hr Ga^{72}. Count the same activity in the standards and calculate the Ga content of the samples.

Note: Aluminum samples were found to contain from 0.02 to 0.1 per cent Ga.

Procedure: [17] *Element determined: Mn, in high alloy steel containing Fe, Ti, Ni, Co, Cr, Ta, Mo, Nb, V and Cu.*

Pre-irradiation treatment: Weigh out duplicate samples of about 300 mg each. Add a known amount of Mn (5 mg as manganous acetate) to one of the samples, mix and pelletize. Encapsulate the samples in Lucite containers.

Irradiation: Irradiate the materials for 10 min in a thermal flux of approximately 10^{10} n cm^{-2} sec^{-1}.

Post-irradiation treatment: Allow the samples to cool for about 4 hr, then place them in the well of a gamma scintillation counter with pulse height discriminator. Count all photons of energies above 1.5 MeV. Take 1 min counts every half hour for 2 hr and also after $\frac{1}{2}$ day, 1 day and 2 days. Extrapolate the long-lived background to the end of the irradiation or some other reference time and subtract from the gross counting data, obtaining the net counting rate from Mn^{56}. Calculate the Mn content from the results obtained with both samples.

Procedure: [18] *Element determined: Gold in platinum.*

Pre-irradiation treatment: Weigh out 0.1 g aliquots of the Pt sample and place the material in silica vials. Add sufficient standard gold solution (100 mg of Au per liter) to provide an additional 20–40 mg of Au to some of the aliquots of Pt. Evaporate solutions to dryness and seal vials. Pack all of the materials in silica wool and seal in aluminum irradiation can.

Irradiation: Irradiate irradiation can for 2.5 hr in a thermal flux of 8×10^{11} n cm^{-2} sec^{-1}.

Post-irradiation treatment: Open the silica vials and transfer the contents to 50 ml glass centrifuge cones containing 10 mg of Au carrier (as $AuCl_3$ in 0.1 M HCl) and 2 ml of 12 M HCl. Wash out the silica tubes with hot 6 M HCl and drain the washings into centrifuge cones containing the activities. Add 1 ml of 16 M HNO_3 to the cones and heat on a water bath until dissolution is complete. Then boil for 10 min, adding two 1 ml portions of 12 M HCl. Adjust the solution to 1 M in HCl and cool. Agitate the solutions with three successive 10 ml portions of ethyl ether and combine the ether extracts. Wash the combined ether phase with two 10 ml portions of 2 M HCl saturated with ether and reject the washings. Heat the ether phase in a centrifuge cone on a water bath to evaporate the ether. Dissolve the residue in 20 ml of hot water,

eat to boiling and add 2 ml of freshly prepared 5 per cent aqueous
ydroquinone solution. Centrifuge and then discard the supernate.
Dissolve the gold in 1 ml of aqua regia, add 1 ml of 12 M HCl and
ilute to 20 ml. Extract with two successive portions of ethyl
cetate, combine the extracts and wash them with two 10 ml
ortions of 2 M HCl. Discard the washings. Then evaporate off
1e ethyl acetate and dissolve the residue in 25 ml of hot 1 M HCl.
Ieat on a water bath, add 2 ml of 5 per cent hydroquinone solu-
on, digest for 10 min and discard the supernate. Wash the
recipitated gold with hot water and then ethanol. Finally, transfer
1e gold to a counting dish using alcohol, dry and weigh. Deter-
1ine the intensity of the 0.411 MeV photopeak from Au^{198} on
gamma scintillation counter, taking care to discriminate against
1e 0.158 and 0.209 MeV Au^{199} photopeaks. Calculate the gold
ontent of the sample from counting data, correcting for chemical
ield.

ote: Platinum sponge specimens showed a Au content from 0.61 to 3.6 ppm.

rocedure:[19] *Element determined: W in high alloy steel containing*
Fe, Co, Ni, Cr, Mo, V, Ta, Mn, Cu and As.
Pre-irradiation treatment: Weigh out steel turnings (10–1000 mg)
nd WO_3 standards, the amounts depending on the W content
nd the available neutron flux. Seal into polyethylene vials.
Irradiation: Irradiate the vials for 1 hr in a thermal flux of
0^7 n cm^{-2} sec^{-1}, as produced by the deuteron bombardment of
eryllium with 11.4 MeV deuterons at a beam current of 100 μA;
he resultant neutrons are thermalized by paraffin.
Post-irradiation treatment: Dissolve the samples in 6 N HCl,
1en add conc HNO_3 dropwise and then 20 ml of conc $HClO_4$.
Ieat the solution on a hot plate to remove HCl and HNO_3, then
ool and add 50 ml of H_2O. Add 2–5 ml of conc H_2O_2 to dissolve
he tungstic acid. Then, add 3 ml of 1 per cent W carrier solution
1s solution of $Na_2WO_4.2 H_2O$) and 5 ml of 1 per cent V carrier
1s solution of Na_3VO_4). Heat on a hot plate to promote the
recipitation of tungstic acid from homogeneous solution. Then
eat for 15 min after the red color of the peroxyvanadic acid has
isappeared, filter off the tungstic acid onto a filter paper and
vash with 3 per cent HNO_3. Dissolve any tungstic acid adhering
o the beaker by washing with a few drops of a mixture of 5 per
ent NaOH and 30 per cent H_2O_2. Precipitate the recovered
ungstic acid and combine with earlier material (recovery over
9 per cent). Determine W by scintillation counting of the 0.48 or
.68 MeV photopeaks from W^{187}, 24 hr half-life.

rocedure:[20] *Element determined: Uranium in beryllium.*
Pre-irradiation treatment: Seal 0.5 g samples of Be into polyethy-
ene vials; then prepare standards by sealing 5 μg of U (100 μl of

solution) into silica ampoules. Seal the samples and standard into an aluminum irradiation can.

Irradiation: Irradiate the can for 1 hr in a thermal flux of 10^{12} cm^{-2} sec^{-1} and let cool for 1–2 days.

Post-irradiation treatment: Place the Be samples in polyethylene cones for counting. Dilute the standard solutions and place volumes similar to that of the samples into polyethylene cones. With a single or multichannel analyzer, determine the 0.106 MeV gamma peak from Np^{239}. Take the decay measurements for 8–1 days to confirm the isotope by its 2.36 day half-life. Calculate the U content of Be from the counting results with the samples and standards.

Notes: 1. Typical Be samples contained 10–16 ppm of U.

2. Np^{239} is produced by the reaction: U^{238} (n, γ) U^{239} $\xrightarrow{\beta}$ Np^{239}.

3. Correction must be made if the isotopic composition of U in Be differs from that of the standard.

Procedure:[21] *Element determined: Selenium in unspecified matrix*

Pre-irradiation treatment: Weigh out the sample (0.1–0.5 g) and the Se standards (0.1–100 μg) and seal into polyethylene vials.

Irradiation: Irradiate the vials for 1 min in a thermal flux of 3×10^{11} n cm^{-2} sec^{-1}.

Post-irradiation treatment: Transfer the samples rapidly to gamma scintillation spectrometer to observe the decay of the 0.162 MeV photopeak from Se^{77m}, half-life 17.5 sec. Plot a decay curve to separate Se^{77m} activity from that of longer half-life, such as Ta^{182m}, Sn^{123} and Ba^{139}.

Note: Se content of various materials ranged from <0.02 ppm for ammonium thiocyanate to 68 ppm for sulfur.

Procedure:[22] *Element determined: Hf in Zr.*

Pre-irradiation treatment: Weigh out 1 g samples of Zr, then 1 g samples of iron powder. Add a known amount of HfO$_2$ to the iron for use as standard samples. Then seal the samples and standards in polyethylene vials.

Irradiation: Irradiate, alternately the samples and standards for 3 min in a thermal flux of 5×10^8 n cm^{-2} sec^{-1} in a training reactor; follow the decay of the 0.215 MeV photopeak from Hf^{179r} (half-life 19 sec). Extrapolate all the counting data to the same reference time and calculate the Hf content of Zr.

Notes: 1 The sensitivity is of the order of 10 ppm and can be increased by the use of a higher neutron flux.

2 The determination of Hf in Zr is difficult by most techniques but relatively simple by neutron activation.

Procedure:[23-25] (*fast neutron activation*) *Element determined: Oxygen in various matrices.*

Pre-irradiation treatment: Weigh out the sample and standard and place each into a separate container of low oxygen content, e.g., polyethylene; insert the container in a pneumatic transfer system and transport it to the irradiation position of a fast neutron generator.

Irradiation: Irradiate the container for 10–30 sec in a flux of 10^8 n cm^{-2} sec^{-1}, then transfer it rapidly to a gamma scintillation spectrometer.

Post-irradiation treatment: Count the combined 6.13 and 7.12 MeV photopeak activity from N^{16} and calculate the oxygen content of samples.

Notes: 1. Levels as low as 10 ppm have been determined.
2. The neutrons of 14 MeV energy are produced by the deuteron bombardment of a tritiated target, taking advantage of a resonance peak near 100 KeV.
3. The reaction with oxygen is: O^{16} (*n*, *p*)N^{16}.
4. No interferences are encountered if the gamma rays below 6 MeV are discriminated against.

NEUTRON ACTIVATION IN CRIMINOLOGY

Neutron activation analysis has in recent years gained some acceptance in criminology. Typical analyses include the establishment of the origin of human hair[26] and the identification of gun powder residues.[27,28] Briefly, the origin of human hair is identified by neutron activation, followed by gamma spectrometry, comparing the relative peak heights from radionuclides of Br, Cl and Na.[26]

The firing of a weapon is established by finding on the suspect's hand by neutron activation analysis evidence of antimony or certain other elements from the igniter cap of the ammunition.[27,28] Following is a typical procedure, based partially on Guinn's work.[28]

Procedure: Elements determined: Antimony, barium and copper in powder residues.

Pre-irradiation treatment: Remove the gun powder residue from the suspect's hand and seal off the residue in a suitable, antimony free container; seal the standards of Sb, Ba and Cu into similar containers and place all the materials in an irradiation can.

Irradiation: Irradiate the can for 30–60 min in a thermal flux of 1.8×10^{12} n cm^{-2} sec^{-1}.

Post-irradiation treatment: Add the carriers, Sb, Ba and Cu to the dissolved residue and perform radiochemical separations for these elements. Determine by gamma spectrometry the Sb^{122}, Ba^{139} and Cu^{64} in the samples and standards and calculate the Sb, Ba and Cu content of the powder specimen.

Procedure:[29] *Element determined: Cadmium in biopsy samples.*

Pre-irradiation treatment: Seal 2–15 mg specimens of human kidney as well as filter paper standards containing 5–10 μg of Cd as $CdSO_4$ into quartz ampoules.

Irradiation: Irradiate the materials for 2–3 days in a thermal flux of 10^{12} n cm^{-2} sec^{-1}.

Post-irradiation treatment: Let the samples cool for a few hours and then place the opened ampoules in beakers containing 1 ml of Cd carrier (10 mg of Cd as sulfate) and 5 ml of fuming HNO_3. Heat the beakers on a water bath until the solutions become clear. Transfer the solutions to 150 ml Erlenmeyer flasks and dilute to 120 ml, making the solutions about 1 M. Bubble H_2S into the solutions to precipitate CdS. Let the solutions stand for several hours and filter through fine porcelain filters, wash the sulfides with a few ml of 1 N NaOH and then water. Determine the Cd^{115} activity by the 0.334 MeV photopeak of its daughter, In^{115m}. Perform the same chemical treatment and counting on the standards. Determine the chemical yield by polarography, precipitation of $CdNH_4PO_4$ or other means. Correct the data for yield and calculate the Cd content of the specimens.

Note: Cd has been determined to a lower limit of 0.4 μg under stated conditions.

CROPS AND FOODS

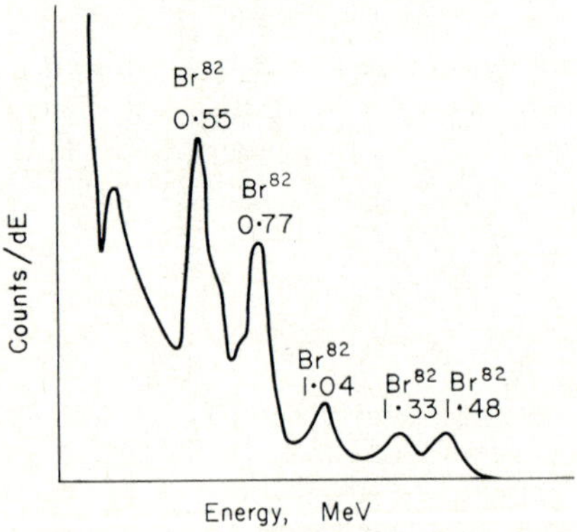

FIG. 5.3 Br^{82} gamma spectrum, obtained by neutron irradiation of wheat, treated with methyl bromide fumigant

Activation analysis has been applied to the analysis of crops and foods in the determinations of fumigants and pesticide residues as well as in the determinations of trace elements. Fig. 5.3 represents the determination of bromide from methyl bromide fumigant in wheat,[30] while Fig. 5.4 represents the determination of chlorine in a food product, the chlorine originating from a chlorinated insecticide.[30] The extraction of chlorine in the latter case assures that no inorganic chlorine is determined.

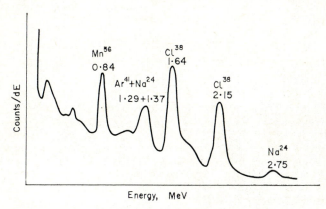

FIG. 5.4   Gamma spectrum of hexane extract of food product, showing Cl^{38}, originating from insecticide

Procedure:[31] *Elements determined: Br, Cl, Mn, Na and K in citrus crops.*

Pre-irradiation treatment: Wash the citrus fruit (oranges) with distilled water, cut in half and collect the orange juice. Weigh 2.5–3.0 g of the juice into polyethylene vials. Add 2.00 μg of Br as NH_4Br to one of the samples for use as a reference. Seal all vials.

Irradiation: Irradiate vials for 30 min in a thermal flux of 1.8×10^{12} n cm^{-2} sec^{-1}.

Post-irradiation treatment: Transfer the contents of vials into un-irradiated vials, place the vials into the well of a gamma ray scintillation spectrometer with a multichannel analyzer, and observe the following photopeaks:

Br^{82} 0.77 MeV,   1.50 day half-life;
Cl^{38} 2.15 MeV,   37.3 min half-life;
Mn^{56} 0.82 MeV,   2.58 hr half-life;
Na^{24} 2.75 MeV,   14.97 hr half-life;
K^{42} 1.53 MeV,   12.4 hr half-life.

6

Record the spectrum at least twice initially, then 30 hr later. Use the early counting data for the determination of Mn and Cl. Then, retaining the "30-hr" count, complement the Na and K activities using suitable standards and print out the remaining Br^{82} spectrum. Calculate the concentration of the desired elements from the counting data, using the added Br as reference.

Notes: 1. Typical concentrations in orange juice were in ppm: Mn 1.8, Na 1.4, K 3.3, Cl 31 and Br 2.0.
2. The results represent total element, organic and inorganic.
3. The analysis of organic bromine requires extraction prior to irradiation.

GEOCHEMISTRY

Neutron activation has been widely used in the determination of trace elements in meteorites and in ores.

Procedure:[32] *Element determined: Potassium in rocks.*
Pre-irradiation treatment: Weigh out 30 mg of the dried and ground potassium acid phthalate standard and about 30 mg of the similarly prepared rock material. Place the materials on polyethylene planchets having an approximate area of 0.8 cm^2 and seal the planchets with ethyl acetate–polystyrene cement.
Irradiation: Irradiate the samples and standards about 6 min in a thermal flux of 5×10^{12} n cm^{-2} sec^{-1}.
Post-irradiation treatment: Let the irradiated materials cool for about 30 hr. Then count the β-radiation using an end window proportional counter and absorbers of about 700 and 2000 mg/cm^2 thickness. (This procedure determines the 3.55 MeV β-rays of K^{42} and permits substraction of Na^{24} γ-radiation). The difference in the counting rates between counts with each absorber is the contribution from K^{42}. Correct the data for decay and calculate the K content by comparison with the phthalate standard.

Note: Rocks in the range of 4–10 per cent K gave results agreeing within $\pm$ 1 per cent absolute with accepted results.

Procedure:[33] *Element determined: Sodium in rocks.*
Pre-irradiation treatment: Weigh out sufficient of the dried samples and Na$_2$CO$_3$ standard material to contain about 3 mg of Na and heat-seal into polyethylene envelopes.
Irradiation: Irradiate for 10 sec to 1 min in a thermal flux of 5×10^{12} n cm^{-2} sec^{-1}.

Post-irradiation treatment: Let the material cool about 24 hr and mount on a planchet or card. Place under a gamma scintillation counter having a solid 2in. × 2in. cylindrical NaI(Tl) crystal (other sizes of crystal may be used) and determine the integral counts above 2.6 MeV. Subtract the blank from the counting data, correct for decay and calculate the Na content of samples by comparison with the Na_2CO_3 standard.

Note: Rocks in the range of 0.050–2.53 per cent Na agreed to within $\pm$ 1–2 per cent absolute with accepted results.

Procedure:[34] *Element determined: Aluminum in rocks.*

Pre-irradiation treatment: Weigh out about 1.5 g of the crushed rock as well as a standard mixture of Al and silica gel into butyrate vials and close them by insertion of polyethylene plugs.

Irradiation: Transfer the vial into a van de Graaff accelerator target assembly (Be target, surrounded by paraffin) and irradiate for 1.0 min at an electron beam current of 0.5 ma (flux of approx. 1×10^8 n cm^{-2} sec^{-1}) and a maximum energy of 2 MeV.

Post-irradiation treatment: Let cool for 0.3 min and count for 1.0 min in a 3in. $\times$ 3in. NaI(Tl) scintillation counter with a single channel analyzer, adjusted to count the 1.78 MeV Al^{28} photopeak. Irradiate and count the standard under similar conditions and calculate the Al content of rock by comparison of the counting data.

Note: Al in rocks at the 0.1 per cent level can be measured to $\pm$ 10 per cent of the true value, with improved accuracy at higher levels or greater neutron flux. The system is designed for the analysis of 30–40 samples per hour.

Procedure:[35] *Elements determined: Scandium and dysprosium in rocks.*

Pre-irradiation treatment: Dissolve the Sc and Dy standards by dissolving their oxides in HNO_3 and diluting to 10^{-1} to $10^2 \mu$g of element per milliliter. Pipet 0.25 ml aliquots onto filter paper and seal the paper into a polyethylene capsule. Seal varying amounts of the 80 mesh sample material (e.g., 3, 10, 30, 100 mg) into polyethylene capsules.

Irradiation: Irradiate the samples and standards for 30 sec in a thermal flux of 4×10^{10} n cm^{-2} sec^{-1}.

Post-irradiation treatment: Let the specimens cool for 10 sec, then count for 30 sec in a well type multichannel scintillation spectrometer, observing the 0.142 MeV Sc^{46m} and 0.108 MeV Dy^{165m} photopeaks on the first half of the memory. Let the sample cool for an additional 30 sec and count again, using the second half of the memory. Calculate the approximate half-life of each nuclide to verify identity (Sc^{146m} 19.5 sec, Dy^{165m} 1.25 min). Using the results from the standards, calculate the Sc and Dy content of the samples.

Note. As little as a few ppm of Sc and Dy have been determined in ores.

PETROLEUM INDUSTRY

The petroleum industry is among the leaders in the application of activation analysis, Such applications include the determination of elements in crudes, gasolines and lubricating oils, in catalysts and in petroleum exploration.

Procedure:[36] *Element determined: Vanadium in crudes.*

Pre-irradiation treatment: Seal 3.0 ml of the crude into a polyethylene container.

Irradiation: Irradiate the capsule for 10 min in a thermal flux of 5×10^{11} n cm^{-2} sec^{-1}.

Post-irradiation treatment: Transfer the sample into a clean vial and place in the well of a gamma scintillation spectrometer. Observe the decay of the 1.44 MeV photopeak from V^{52} (half-life 3.77 min). From a knowledge of the neutron dosage or from a comparison with the standards, calculate the V content of the crude.

Note: V at levels as low as 0.1 ppm can be determined without chemical separation.

Activation analysis is widely used in petroleum exploration although the analytical chemist is not generally involved in such work. Because the techniques used in such exploration may find wider application, some information is presented here.

Prompt gamma rays, emitted as a result of irradiation with fast neutrons, are used to identify elements in bore holes. The pertinent information compiled by Caldwell,[37] is summarized in Table 5.2. It is to be noted that prompt gamma rays can be used to obtain carbon/oxygen and carbon/hydrogen ratios, thus furnishing a measure of the relative concentration of water and oil.

TABLE 5.2. PROMPT GAMMA-RAYS FROM IRRADIATION WITH FAST NEUTRONS

Element irradiated	Activated nuclide	Gamma-ray energy, MeV
Mg	Mg^{24}	1.37
Si	Si^{28}	1.78
H (H_2O and oil)	H^1	2.2
S	S^{32}	2.25
Ca	Ca^{40}	3.73
C (element and oil)	C^{12}	4.4
O (H_2O)	O^{16}	6.7

Measurements with fast-neutron produced prompt gamma rays are made by lowering a logging source (accelerator probe or isotopic source) and a scintillation counter into the borehole. As a result of the irradiation with fast neutrons, certain (n, p) reactions offer further opportunities for analytical data. Examples include Al, O and Si.

Thermal neutron activation of sedimentary rock specimens for Al, Ca, Cl, Fe, Mg, Na, P and Ti has been reported by Caldwell and Mills.[38] The rapid analysis of catalysts for many elements has been reported by Guinn and Wagner.[39]

SEMI-CONDUCTORS

The proper functioning of semi-conductors and thermionic materials requires maintenance of closely held tolerances in concentration of impurities and additives. Thus, chemical analyses must be performed for a number of elements at low concentrations. Cali and Weiner[40] have discussed the attainable sensitivity in the activation analysis for elements of interest to electronic material scientists. Gebauhr[41,42] has studied production processes and presented schematically a plan for the separation and determination of impurities in semi-conductor materials. This scheme is shown in Fig. 5.5. Extensive use is made of gamma spectrometry following chemical separation.

Procedure:[43] *Element determined: Iodine in silicon.*
Pre-irradiation treatment: Weigh out Si samples of about 1 g each and then weigh out a small amount of KI standard. Seal all the materials into polyethylene vials.
Irradiation: Irradiate the samples and standard for 1 hr in a thermal flux of 6×10^{11} n cm^{-2} sec^{-1}.
Post-irradiation treatment: Powder the silicon sample in an iron mortar immediately after irradiation, then add a weighed amount of Si (about 0.8 g) to a molten bath of 10 g of KOH, containing 5 mg of I carrier (as KI). Heat to obtain complete dissolution. Then dissolve the cooled melt with 100 ml of 5 N H_2SO_4, containing a few mg of NaCl and KBr holdback carriers. Add a solution of $NaNO_2$ and distill the liberated I_2 into a receiver containing a dilute solution of Na_2SO_3. Oxidize the iodide to I_2 by treating the distillate with H_2SO_4 and $NaNO_2$ and then extract the I_2 into the xylene. Wash the organic phase with dilute H_2SO_4 and water. Back-extract the I_2 into an aqueous phase containing Na_2SO_3 and then add acetic acid, silver nitrate and HNO_3 to the aqueous

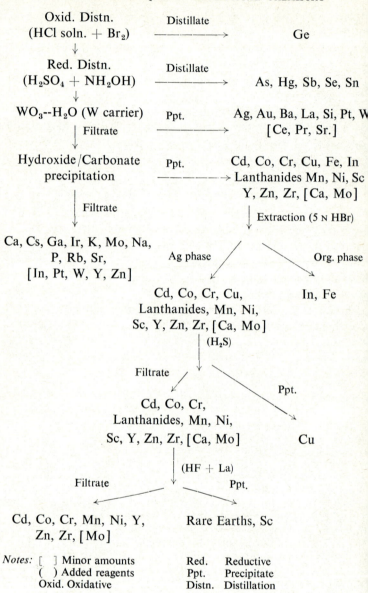

Fig. 5.5. Group scheme for the separation of elements in semi-conductor materials.

phase to precipitate the AgI. Filter the AgI onto a weighed glass filter, wash with very dilute HNO_3, then H_2O, ethanol and finally ether. Weigh and count the I^{128} β activity on a Geiger–Müller or windowless proportional counter. Dissolve the irradiated KI standard, oxidize with $NaNO_2$, extract into xylene and proceed as previously. Count in the same manner as the samples.

Notes: 1. The iodine content of silicon was shown to range from 0.005–4.5 ppm, depending on the degree of purification.
2. In cases where the iodine content is at least a few ppm and no interfering γ-emitters are present, γ- spectrometry on the unseparated Si may prove satisfactory.
3. The author[43] indicated a lower limit of detection of about 0.002 ppm, using a flux of 6×10^{11} n cm^{-2} sec^{-1}.

SPACE EXPLORATION

Finally, one must consider the use of activation analysis in space exploration, where initially at least, much of the work will have to be performed by remote techniques. Monaghan and co-authors[44] have proposed fast neutron activation for the analysis of the lunar surface. The use of a fast neutron accelerator and gamma spectrometer is proposed, using techniques that are familiar to workers in petroleum exploration.

REFERENCES

1. A. A. SMALES, *Atomics*, **4**, 55 (1953).
2. D. GIBBONS, B. A. LOVERIDGE and R. J. MILLETT, U.K. Atomic Energy Research Establ. Rept. AERE-I/R-2208 (1957).
3. D. GIBBONS, D. MAPPER, R. J. MILLETT and H. SIMPSON, U.K. Atomic Energy Research Establ. Rept. AERE-I/R-2208, Suppl. I (1960).
4. R. C. KOCH, *Activation Analysis Handbook*, Academic Press, New York (1960).
5. D. F. C. MORRIS, *Met Revs.*, **7**, 241 (1962).
6. A. A. SMALES and L. R. WAGER (Eds.), *Methods in Geochemistry*, Interscience, New York (1960).
7. M. J. AITKEN, V. M. EMELEUS, E. T. HALL and C. M. KRAAY, in *Radioisotopes in the Physical Sciences and Industry*, Vol. II, International Atomic Energy Agency, Vienna (1962).
8. J. S. BECK and T. R. MANNEY, *Science*, **137**, 865 (1962).
9. D. G. KAISER and W. W. MEINKE, *Talanta*, **3**, 255 (1960).
10. P. B. van ZANTEN, D. DECAT and G. LELIAERT, *Talanta*, **9**, 213 (1962).
11. D. GIBBONS, *Int. J. Appl. Radn. Isotopes*, **4**, 45 (1958).
12. R. FUKAI and W. W. MEINKE, *Limnology and Oceanography*, **7**, 186 (1962).
13. D. C. BORG, R. E. SEGEL, P. KIENLE and L. CAMPBELL, *Int. J. Appl. Radn. Isotopes*, **11**, 10 (1961).

14. H. Tsuji, Y. Kusaka and Y. Namikawa, *Bull. Chem. Soc. Japan*, **35**, 2045 (1962).
15. F. Girardi and R. Pietra, *Anal. Chem.*, **35**, 173 (1963).
16. W. Kiesl, H. Bildstein and H. Sorantin, *Mikrochim. Acta*, 151 (1963).
17. P. Bouten and J. Hoste, *Talanta*, **8**, 322 (1961).
18. D. F. C. Morris and R. A. Killick, *Talanta*, **8**, 793 (1961).
19. G. Leliaert, J. Hoste and Z. Eeckhaut, *Talanta*, **2**, 115 (1959).
20. A. A. Smales, D. Mapper and A. P. Seyfang, *Anal. Chim. Acta*, **25**, 587 (1961).
21. M. Okada, *Nature*, **187**, 594 (1960).
22. T. Stribel, *Z. angew. Phys.*, **9**, 293 (1957).
23. R. A. Stallwood, W. E. Mott and D. T. Fanale, *Anal. Chem.*, **35**, 6 (1963).
24. R. F. Coleman, *Analyst*, **87**, 590 (1962).
25. W. W. Meinke and R. W. Shideler, *Nucleonics*, **20**, No. 3, 60 (1962).
26. J. P. W. Houtman, *Kerntechnik*, **4**, 53 (1962).
27. F. Baumgärtner and A. Schöntag, *Kerntechnik*, **4**, 51 (1962).
28. V. P. Guinn, in *Radiation News, Nucleonics*, **21**, No. 1, 28 (1963).
29. T. Westermark and B. Sjöstrand, *Int. J. Appl. Radn. Isotopes*, **9**, 78 (1960)
30. J. D Buchanan and V. P. Guinn, *Food Technology*, **17**, 17 (1963).
31. C. E. Castro and R. A. Schmitt, *J. Agr. Food Chem.*, **10**, 236 (1962).
32. J. W. Winchester, *Anal. Chem.*, **33**, 1007 (1961).
33. G. L. Schroeder and J. W. Winchester, *Anal. Chem.*, **34**, 96 (1962).
34. D. F. Rhodes and W. E. Mott, *Anal. Chem.*, **34**, 1507 (1962).
35. M. Okada, *Anal. Chem.*, **33**, 1949 (1961).
36. W. W. Meinke, U.S. Atomic Energy Comm. Rept. AECU-3887 (1958).
37. R. L. Caldwell, *Nucleonics*, **16**, No. 12, 58 (1958).
38. R. L. Caldwell and W. R. Mills, Jr., *Nuclear Instr. and Methods*, **5**, 312 (1959).
39. V. P. Guinn and C. D. Wagner, *Anal. Chem.*, **32**, 317 (1960).
40. J. P. Cali and J. R. Weiner, *J. Electrochem, Soc.*, **107**, 1017 (1960).
41. W. Gebauhr and J. Martin, *Int. J. Appl. Radn. Isotopes*, **4**, 173 (1959).
42. W. Gebauhr, *Kerntechnik*, **4**, 323 (1962).
43. T. Nozaki, H. Baba and H. Araki, *Bull. Chem. Soc. Japan*, **33**, 320 (1960).
44. R. Monaghan, A. H. Youmans, R. A. Bergan and E. C. Hopkinson, *I.E.E.E. Trans. on Nuclear Sci.*, **NS–10**, 183 (1963).

CHAPTER 6

POSITIVE ION AND GAMMA RAY ACTIVATION ANALYSIS

ALTHOUGH neutron activation analysis has found much wider use than have positive ion and gamma-ray activation analysis, there are, nevertheless, many cases where greater specificity or greater sensitivity is achieved by these other activating fluxes. For example, the low penetrating ability of positive ions into matter can be utilized in the analysis of surface layers.

A typical requirement in semi-conductor research is the analysis of boron on the surface of silicon. Neutron activation is out of question owing to the penetrating nature of neutrons and the short half-life of the activation products. The reaction B^{11} (p, n) C^{11} has a relatively large cross section, 1.0 mb, for 2.83 MeV protons, compared to the cross section for potentially interfering reactions such as N^{14} (p, α) C^{11}. Busch et al.[1] have irradiated silicon specimens, 5 mm diameter $\times$ 1 mm thickness with 3 MeV protons and observed the decay of the 20.4 min C^{11} by measuring its 0.51 MeV positron annihilation radiation. The limit of detection was established as 4×10^{14} boron atoms cm^{-2}. A depth of $11 \pm 5\mu$ was activated. Increase of the proton energy to 3.7 MeV would increase the sensitivity 60-fold. It is interesting to note that the boron layer containing 3.4×10^{16} atoms cm^{-2} originates from Pyrex glass from the vacuum system! The boron layer was found to be less than 30μ thick.

The oxide film thickness on tantalum foil has been analyzed by Thompson,[2] using protons of 4 MeV energy and a 10μA beam current. The reaction is O^{18} (p, n) F^{18}. The position annihilation radiation, 0.51 MeV from the decay of 1.87 hr F^{18} was counted. The maximum film thickness for the analysis with 4 MeV protons was estimated as 25μ.

Fogelström-Fineman et al.[3] have performed tracer studies in photosynthesis using isotopically-enriched O^{18} and determined this isotope by proton irradiation in the same manner as Thompson.[2]

Part per billion levels of some elements have been analyzed in Be, Th and Mylar by He^3 bombardment using particles of energies from 8–31 MeV[4,5]. The low binding energy of the He^4 nucleus results in the exoergic behavior of many nuclear reactions, permitting reactions by 8 MeV ions with most elements below Sc in the periodic table. The oxygen was determined by the reaction, O^{16} (He^3, p) F^{18}, where the positron annihilation radiation from F^{18} was measured.

Positive ion bombardment is used extensively in geochemical investigations. Sippel and Glover[6] have reported the analysis of Li, Be, B, C, F, Na, Mg, Al and P by proton, deuteron and alpha irradiations using a 2 MeV van de Graaff positive ion accelerator. Table 6.1, abstracted from Sippel and Glover's paper, provides an adequate summary of their work. Sedimentary rock samples were ground to 325 mesh and pressed to pellets of $\frac{5}{8}$in. diameter $\times$ 0.070in. thickness; these weighed about 830 mg. The measurements were performed with a coincidence gamma ray spectrometer, Geiger–Müller counter, BF_3 and Li^6 I neutron detectors.

TABLE 6.1. RESULTS OF BOMBARDMENT OF SYNTHETIC ROCKS WITH 2 MeV POSITIVE IONS[6]

Element	Reaction	Product analyzed	Half-life of product	Estimated limit of detection, %*
Li	Li^7(p, n) Be^7	prompt n	—	0.01
Be	Be^9(α, n γ) C^{12}	prompt γ	—	0.01
B	B^{10}(α, n) N^{13}	N^{13}	10.0 min	0.1
C	C^{12}(d, n) N^{13}	N^{13}	10.0 min.	0.005
F	F^{19}(p, α) O^{16}	prompt γ	—	0.01
Na	Na^{23}(d, p) Na^{24}	Na^{24}	14.97 hr	0.01
Mg	Mg^{26}(d, p) Mg^{27}	Mg^{27}	9.45 min	0.05
Al	Al^{27}(d, p) Al^{28}	Al^{28}	2.3 min	0.02
P	P^{31}(d, p) P^{32}	P^{32}	14.6 days	0.01

Note: $\leq$ 400 μ coulombs per target.

Certain elements exhibit low activation thresholds for alpha particle capture. Thus, the elements Be, F, B, Na, Mg and Al undergo reactions with 5 MeV alpha particles, emitted by many isotopic sources. Table 6.2 lists pertinent nuclear date for irradiation with Po^{210} alpha particles[7].

TABLE 6.2 PROPERTIES OF ALPHA-PARTICLE INDUCED REACTIONS[7]

Target	Reaction	Product	Half-life of product	Activation cross section for 5 MeV particles, mb
Be	α, n γ	C^{12}	very short, count during irradiation	400
F	α, n	Na^{22}	2.60 years	—
B	α, n	N^{13}	10.0 min	32 (1.51 MeV)
Na	α, n	Al^{26}	6.5 sec	—
Mg	α, p	Al^{28}	2.3 min	—
Al	α, n	P^{30}	2.55 min	20

It has often been pointed out by Odeblad and Odeblad[8] that no other elements will give appreciable yields in radio-isotopes when irradiated with 5 MeV alpha particles. If the 6.5 sec Al^{26} activity is allowed to decay before counting and the 2.6 year Na^{22} activity is neglected, then only B, Mg and Al are of concern. Al^{28} decays with the emission of beta rays and 1.78 MeV gamma rays. N^{13} and P^{30} decay by positron emission. Thus, the method is specific for Mg, if the 1.78 MeV gamma ray is counted. The positron emitters can be analyzed by decay curves. Odeblad and Odeblad[8] have used a Po^{210} alpha source, ranging from 160 to 15 mc for the determination of Al in several alloys. A Geiger–Müller counter served to detect the induced activity. The procedure involved a 5 min irradiation, a 20-sec cooling time and a 5-min counting time.

Beryllium on filter paper has been determined by irradiation with Po^{210} alpha particles and simultaneous counting of the 4.43 MeV γ-transition to the C^{12} ground state.[9] With a 5 curie source and an NaI(Tl) scintillation counter, deposits of the order of $1\mu g$ were determined.

Although low-energy alpha activation analysis has not been employed to an appreciable extent, the foregoing information has been presented to permit the chemist to give adequate consideration to this interesting technique.

TABLE 6.3. PHOTONUCLEAR ACTIVATION DATA*

Target element	Product nuclide	Half-life	Activity produced per μg of element 20 MeV	25 MeV
C	C^{11}	20.4 min	4.4×10^3	1.8×10^5
N	N^{13}	10.0 min	2.0×10^1	8.9×10^1
O	O^{15}	1.97 min	8.9×10^3	6.7×10^4
F	F^{17}	1.2 min	1.6×10^3	1.6×10^3
F	F^{18}	1.87 hr	1.6×10^4	3.3×10^4
Ne	Ne^{19}	18.2 sec	2.2×10^1	1.2×10^2
Na	Na^{22}	2.60 years	4.4	8.9
Mg	Na^{24}	14.97 hr	2.0×10^2	1.0×10^3
Mg	Na^{25}	1.0 min	2.2×10^3	2.0×10^4
Mg	Mg^{23}	11.9 sec	2.2×10^4	1.3×10^5
Al	Al^{26}	6.5 sec	1.1×10^5	2.9×10^5
Si	Al^{28}	2.30 min	4.4×10^3	2.0×10^4
Si	Al^{29}	6.56 min	1.3×10^3	1.1×10^4
Si	Si^{27}	4.9 sec	3.3×10^4	1.3×10^5
P	P^{30}	2.55 min	1.3×10^5	2.4×10^5
S	P^{30}	2.55 min	4.4×10^3	4.4×10^3
S	S^{31}	3.2 sec	4.0×10^4	1.6×10^5
Ar	Cl^{39}	55.5 min	1.3×10^2	8.9×10^2
Ca	Ca^{39}	1.06 sec	2.0×10^4	8.9×10^4
V	Sc^{47}	3.43 days	2.9×10^1**	
Cr	V^{52}	3.77 min	4.4×10^3	1.1×10^4
Cr	Cr^{49}	41.9 min	6.7×10^3	1.3×10^4
Mn	Mn^{54}	0.850 years	5.5×10^1	7.8×10^1
Fe	Fe^{53}	8.9 min	1.3×10^4	3.5×10^4
Fe	Fe^{55}	2.94 years	8.9	2.0×10^1
Ni	Co^{57}	0.740 years	2.9	1.1×10^1
Co	Co^{58}	72 days	1.7×10^2	3.3×10^2
Cu	Co^{61}	1.65 hr	2.2×10^2	9.3×10^2
Ni	Ni^{57}	1.5 days	3.1×10^3	6.7×10^3
Cu	Cu^{61}	3.33 hr	—	3.1×10^3
Cu	Cu^{62}	9.8 min	5.3×10^5	5.3×10^5
Cu	Cu^{64}	12.9 hr	1.6×10^4	2.9×10^4
Zn	Zn^{63}	38.3 min	2.4×10^5	5.5×10^5
As	As^{73}	76 days	6.7	5.3×10^1
As	As^{74}	17.5 days	8.9×10^2	1.2×10^3
Br	As^{77}	1.6 days	1.6	7.8
Br	Br^{78}	6.4 min	2.7×10^5	3.5×10^5
Br	Br^{80}	18 min	2.0×10^5	4.0×10^5

TABLE 6.3 — *continued*

Target element	Product nuclide	Half-life	Activity produced per μg of element 20 MeV	25 MeV
Br	Br^{80m}	4.58 hr	1.3×10^4	2.4×10^4
Rb	Br^{83}	2.33 hr	3.8	8.9×10^1
Rb	Rb^{86}	19.5 days	3.1×10^2	6.4×10^2
Sr	Sr^{85}	65 days	2.4×10^1	4.0×10^1
Y	Y^{88}	2.0 hr	1.6×10^4	2.2×10^4
Zr	Zr^{89}	4.4 min	4.7×10^5	8.9×10^5
Zr	Zr^{89m}	79.3 hr	4.4×10^3	8.9×10^3
Nb	Nb^{92}	21.6 hr	2.4×10^4	3.8×10^4
Mo	Nb^{97}	1.2 hr	2.2×10^3	2.2×10^4
Mo	Nb^{99}	2.5 min	4.4×10^2	4.4×10^3
Mo	Mo^{91}	1.2 min	8.9×10^3	1.8×10^4
Mo	Mo^{91m}	15.5 min	4.7×10^4	8.9×10^4
Mo	Mo^{99}	2.75 days	1.3×10^3	1.8×10^3
Rh	Rh^{102}	0.575 years	1.1×10^2	1.7×10^2
Ag	Ag^{105}	40 days	8.9	4.4×10^1
Ag	Ag^{106}	24 min	4.4×10^5	6.6×10^5
Ag	Ag^{108}	2.4 min	4.4×10^5	6.6×10^5
Cd	Ag^{112}	3.2 hr	4.4×10^2	4.4×10^3
In	In^{113m}	1.7 hr	4.9×10^4	1.2×10^5
In	In^{114}	1.2 min	2.2×10^5	3.1×10^5
In	In^{114m}	50 days	8.2×10^2	1.2×10^3
In	In^{115m}	4.5 hr	7.8×10^2	1.0×10^3
Sn	In^{117}	2.5 hr	2.2×10^2	2.2×10^3
Sb	Sb^{120}	16.5 min	5.3×10^5	6.7×10^5
Sb	Sb^{122}	2.8 days	6.7×10^3	8.9×10^3
I	I^{126}	13.0 days	1.8×10^3	2.4×10^3
Ta	Ta^{179}	1.6 years	1.8	8.9
Ta	Ta^{180m}	8.15 hr	8.9×10^4	1.3×10^5
Au	Au^{195}	0.49 years	8.9	1.6×10^1
Au	Au^{196}	5.55 days	4.4×10^3	6.7×10^3
Au	Au^{197m}	7.4 sec	6.7×10^3	8.9×10^3
Pb	Tl^{207}	4.8 min	$8.9 \times 10^{2**}$	
Th	Th^{231}	1.04 days	2.9×10^4	4.9×10^4
U	U^{237}	6.75 days	4.4×10^3	6.7×10^3

*Table prepared by use of data from M. H. MACGREGOR, *Nucleonics* **15**, No. 11, 176 (1957).

Results apply for irradiation of one hour or saturation, at a power level of 10 kW, target 3in. from tungsten converter. Sensitivity is expressed in disintegrations min^{-1} μg^{-1} of element, except for gases where it is expressed as disintegrations min^{-1} 10^{-6} cm^{-3}.

**Measured at 23 MeV.

PHOTONUCLEAR REACTIONS

It was stated earlier that photoexcitation of Be^9 can produce neutrons. In the example cited, Sb^{124} furnishes the photons. The threshold for the reaction is 1.66 MeV. The only other nuclide to undergo such a reaction at a photon energy below 5 MeV is H^2 (deuterium), with a threshold of 2.23 MeV. Use has been made of these reactions in the analysis of beryllium and deuterium, as will be shown later.

The majority of elements have thresholds for (γ, n) reactions in the range of 10–20 MeV. Photons in this energy range are available from accelerators such as a betatron and linear accelerator. The energy spectra of photoneutrons, resulting from the irradiation of elements with 20–25 MeV Bremsstrahlung, have been investigated by several authors[10-12]. Table 6.3 shows specific activities, in disintegrations min^{-1} μg^{-1} of element, obtained by irradiation with Bremsstrahlung of maximum energies of 20 and 25 MeV. As pointed out by McGregor, the sensitivity can be further increased by moving the sample closer to the tungsten converter and by using thicker samples. Self-shielding is relatively insignificant owing to the penetrating nature of Bremsstrahlung and the relatively low capture cross sections of the elements. The directional nature of the Bremsstrahlung beam results in large fluxes and high sensitivities, as shown in Table 6.3. Photonuclear reactions can be highly useful, where thermal neutron activation gives difficulties on account of interfering reactions, low cross sections and short half-lives.

For example, the reaction Al^{27} (n, α) Na^{24} masks the reaction Na^{23} (n, γ) Na^{24}, when thermal neutrons are used; the reaction Na^{23} (γ, n) Na^{22} yields a clearly identifiable product. Carbon is not activated by neutrons below 20 MeV in energy, while the reaction C^{12} (γ, n) C^{11} gives a high yield with 20 MeV photons; the product, with its 20 min half-life, is readily counted.

Albert et al.[13] have given preliminary results for the photonuclear analysis of oxygen, carbon and nitrogen in metals, using a linear accelerator of maximum energy of 30 MeV. It is pointed out that these elements can be analyzed selectively by taking advantage of their different reaction thresholds. Table 6.4 gives the relative specific activities and thresholds. The products range in half-life from 2 to 20 min.

TABLE 6.4. PHOTONUCLEAR ACTIVATION DATA[13]

Electron energy, MeV	Relative specific activity and threshold		
	Oxygen, 16.6 MeV	Carbon, 18.7 MeV	Nitrogen, 10.5 MeV
15	0	0	4
16	0.2	0	—
18	100	0	—
19	200	0.2	20
20	300	100	—

Albert et al.[13] obtained sensitivities of 10 ppm for oxygen, and carbon, and 100 ppm for nitrogen; in all cases, the 0.51 MeV positron annihilation radiation was counted. The separation of nitrogen by a Kjeldahl distillation would increase the sensitivity for nitrogen but it would be difficult to perform rapidly. No procedures will be given here for photonuclear reactions as they have thus far found relatively little analytical application. The analytical chemist in industry may have access to a betatron or similar accelerator and may find it highly desirable to undertake photonuclear activation analysis.

Recently, studies on the formation of metastable isomers using photoactivation with 3 MeV Bremsstrahlung have shown that this technique offers some promise as an analytical tool.[14] The results of this study are summarized in Table 6.5, where specific activities are expressed as counts min/mg of element. No interference was encountered from elements between atomic numbers 4–32. The short half-life of many products necessitated the use of a fast sample transfer device. With respect to the use of this technique, it ought to be noted that this little-used approach to analysis will undoubtedly find wider acceptance owing to its selectivity.

The low threshold for the photo-activation of Be has led to the use of this technique for the detection and determination of the element. Thus, Levine and Surls[15] have used Bremsstrahlung from the irradiation of a tungsten target with 2.1 MeV electrons from a van de Graaff accelerator for the determination of Be in ores. The neutrons, resulting from the reaction $Be^9 (\gamma, n) 2\alpha$, were

TABLE 6.5 PHOTOACTIVATION OF METASTABLE ISOMERS*

Target element	Principal activity	Half-life	Specific activity cpm mg^{-1} of element	Photon energies KeV
Se	Se^{77m}	18 sec	140	160
Sr	Sr^{87m}	2.8 hr	20	380
Y	Y^{89m}	16 sec	6	890
Rh	Rh^{103m}	57 min	0.8	21
Ag	Ag^{109m}	40 sec	200	90
Cd	Cd^{111m}	50 min	130	140, 230
In	In^{115m}	4.2 hr	300	150, 330
Ba	Ba^{137m}	2.7 min	1.6	660
Er	Er^{167m}	2.5 sec	300	210
Lu	Lu^{176m}	3.8 hr	10	86
Hf	Hf^{179m}	20 sec	4000	65, 220
Ir	Ir^{191m}	6 sec	1000	130
Pt	Pt^{195m}	4.1 days	1	69
Au	Au^{197m}	7.4 sec	400	70, 270
Hg	Hg^{199m}	42 min	2	74, 155, 390

*Irradiation conditions:
    One hour irradiation with Bremsstrahlung from 3 MeV, 1 mA electrc
    beam; average photon flux 3×10^{13} photons cm^{-2} sec^{-1}; samples dissolve
    in aqueous or organic solution; counting performed on 100 channel NaI(T
    gamma spectrometer.

thermalized in polyethylene and the thermal neutron flux induce
the activity in a silver disc. The Ag^{108} and Ag^{110} activities wer
counted with a Geiger–Müller counter. A cycle of 80 sec irradia
tion, 10 sec transfer time and 30 sec counting time gave a lim
of detection of 20 ppm of Be with a 20 g sample.

The photo-activation of Be is widely used in field exploratio
for Be, with a Sb^{124} gamma source for excitation and measuremer
of the resulting neutrons with a boron trifluoride proportiona
counter, or an activated phosphor with photomultiplier tub
Bowie et al.[16] have described a field beryllium detection instru
ment using BF$_3$ detectors and an Sb^{124} source of 100 mc strength
The limit of detection was established at approximately 5 ppm c
BeO. Measurements were made in situ with the instrument place
in direct contact with the minerals.

The low threshold for the (γ, n) reaction with deuterium, 2.2
MeV, was mentioned earlier. Faires et al.[17] have used a 1-curi
source of Na^{24} to determine 0.1 per cent D$_2$O in 25 ml of H$_2$C
to ± 2 per cent.

REFERENCES

1. G. BUSCH, H. SCHADE, A. GOBBI and P. MARMIER, *J. Phys. Chem., Solids*, **23**, 513 (1962).
2. B. A. THOMPSON, *Anal. Chem.*, **33**, 583 (1961).
3. I. FOGELSTRÖM-FINEMAN, O. HOLM-HANSEN, B. M. TOLBERT and M. CALVIN, *Int. J. Appl. Radn. Isotopes*, **2**, 280 (1957).
4. S. S. MARKOWITZ and J. D. MAHONY, *Anal. Chem.*, **34**, 329 (1962).
5. S. S. MARKOWITZ and J. D. MAHONY, U.S. Atomic Energy Comm. Rept. UCRL-9908 (1961).
6. R. F. SIPPEL and E. D. GLOVER, *Nucl. Instr. and Meth.*, **9**, 37 (1960).
7. R. C. KOCH, *Activation Analysis Handbook*, Academic Press, New York (1960).
8. E. ODEBLAD and S. ODEBLAD, *Anal. Chim. Acta*, **15**, 1141 (1956).
9. R. GOLD, *Nucleonics*, **15**, No. 11, 114 (1957).
10. G. A. PRICE, *Phys. Rev.*, **93**, 1279 (1954).
11. M. H. MACGREGOR, *Nucleonics*, **15**, No. 11, 176 (1957).
12. K. STRAUCH, *Ann. Rev. Nucl. Sci.*, **2**, 105 (1953).
13. P. ALBERT, C. ENGELMANN, S. MAY and J. PETIT, *Comptes rendus*, **254**, 119 (1962).
14. H. R. LUKENS, Jr., J. W. ORVOS and C. D. WAGNER, *Int. J. Appl. Radn. Isotopes*. **11**, 30 (1961).
15. C. A. LEVINE and J. P. SURLS, Jr., *Anal. Chem.*, **34**, 1614 (1962).
16. S. H. V. BOWIE, H. BISBY, K. C. BURKE and F. H. HALE, *Trans. Institution of Mining and Metallurgy*, **69**, Pt. 7, 345 (1959–60).
17. R. A. FAIRES, J. E. JOHNSTON and R. J. MILLETT, *Nucleonics*, **12**, No. 10, 48 (1954).

CHAPTER 7

RADIATION SCATTERING AND ABSORPTION

ABSORPTION resonances and scattering, arising from the exposure of a material to various radiations and particles, are phenomena which have analytical applications.

Meinke[1] has listed some elements and their thermal neutron absorption cross sections with emphasis on the determination of elements by neutron absorption. The information is presented in Table 7.1.

TABLE 7.1. THERMAL NEUTRON ABSORPTION CROSS SECTIONS

Element	Absorption cross section, barns	Element	Absorption cross section, barns
Gd	46,000	Tm	118
Sm	5500	Hf	112
Eu	4600	Lu	108
Cd	2550	Au	98
Dy	1100	Re	84
B	750	Li	71
Ir	430	Ho	64
Hg	380	Ag	62
In	190	Nd	46
Rh	150	Tb	44

It must be pointed out that these cross sections are for elements with their natural isotopic abundances. For example, lithium is normally composed of 7.5 per cent Li^6 ($\sigma = 950$ barns) and 92.5 per cent Li^7 ($\sigma = 0.033$ barn), resulting in a cross section for natural Li of 70 barns. However, the isotopic composition of commercially available Li may have been altered by removal of a significant part of its Li^6. The chemist is therefore cautioned about the effect of isotopic composition of an element on its neutron absorption cross section. Unless the composition is known, standards should be prepared from the same lot of material.

The isotopic composition of some boron hydrides has been determined by neutron absorption by Hamlen and Koski.[2]

Commonly, thermal neutron absorption measurements are made by measuring the relative transmission of neutrons through the sample, using a BF_3 counter as detector. Samples are best placed in plastic containers, avoiding high cross section materials such as borated glass. The technique lends itself to use with isotopic neutron sources, provided sufficient material is available. A review of the data in Table 7.1 will guide the chemist in arriving at a decision concerning the applicability of neutron absorption. A more complete compilation of neutron cross sections has been prepared by Hughes.[3,4]

The measurement of the thermal neutron absorption cross section of a material by its effect on the reactivity of a nuclear reactor, called "Danger Coefficient Method", has been utilized to determined elements of high absorption cross section. Such analyses include the determination of boron and the U^{235} content of uranium. Low power reactors[5] and critical assemblies[6] have been employed in analyses by danger coefficients.

Neutron absorption resonances, characteristic of a particular nucleus, have been used in the determination of some elements. The neutron cross section spectrum of iridium, shown in Fig. 6.5, has a resonance peak at 6.6 eV. This resonance absorption can be used to determine quantitatively elements such as iridium in the presence of many other elements. The technique requires the use of an intense neutron source such as a reactor or a cyclotron and neutron spectrometer. The details concerning this technique have been compiled by Taylor et al.[7,8]

The slowing down (moderation) of fast neutrons by elastic collisions with atoms of low mass is a function of the mass of the scattering medium. Table 7.2, compiled by Hughes,[9] gives the average number of collisions required to slow down 2 MeV neutrons to thermal energy (0.025 eV).

The high slowing-down power of hydrogen is the basis of a number of commercial applications for the determination of hydrogen in the form of water as well as other forms. Basically, such a device consists of a source of fast neutrons, such as a Ra–Be source, a sample chamber and a thermal neutron detector such as a BF_3 counter. The source is usually surrounded by the test material.

TABLE 7.2. MODERATING ABILITY OF MATERIALS

Material	Mass No.	Average number of collisions	Slowing down power
H	1	18	1.000
H^2	2	25	0.725
Be	9	87	0.209
C	12	115	0.158
U	238	2180	0.0084

The source strength ranges from 1 mc to several curies, with sources of a few millicuries in common use.

The determination of moisture in wood and minerals has been described thoroughly by Kühn.[10] Van Bavel[11] has reported on surface soil measurement for moisture. The measurement of moisture in 3200 lb. charges of sand in a foundry has been described by Burley et al.[12]

The scattering of positive ions by solid surfaces has been used by Rubin[13] to determine elements to a depth of a few micron with sensitivities of 10^{-8} to 10^{-6} g cm^{-2}. This technique is based on measurement of the momentum distribution of protons scattered from the solid surface. Fig. 7.1 shows the basic features of Rubin's apparatus.[13] Analytical data, obtained by bombard-

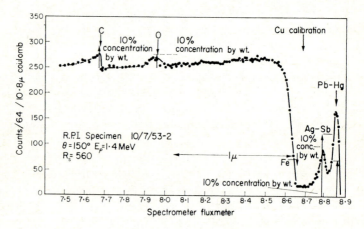

FIG. 7.1 Schematic drawing of apparatus used for scattering analyses

ment of a steel sample with 1.4 MeV protons, are shown in Fig. 7.2. The limited range of protons in solids permits the determination of the physical structure of thin films down to $10^{-2}\mu$ in thickness.

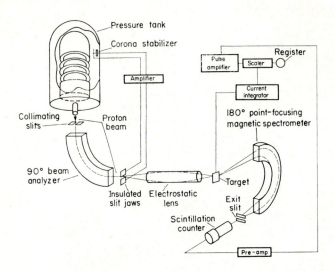

FIG. 7.2 Momentum distribution of scattering from a steel sample exposed to high temperature propellant gases

Absorption and backscattering of alpha, beta and gamma radiation are widely used in industrial process control in thickness gauges, level gauges, gas chromatographs and many other applications. Such applications have been described elsewhere.[14,15]

REFERENCES

1. W. W. MEINKE, *Talanta*, **5**, 264 (1960).
2. R. P. HAMLEN and W. S. KOSKI, *Anal. Chem.*, **28**, 1631 (1956).
3. D. J. HUGHES, *Neutron Cross Sections*, Pergamon Press, New York (1957).
4. D. J. HUGHES and R. B. SCHWARTZ, U.S. Atomic Energy Comm. Rept. BNL-325 (1958); and supplements.
5. M. B. GUSTAVSON and J. C. SHERWIN, in U.S. Atomic Energy Comm. Rept. TID-7560 (1958).
6. E. FAST, D. W. KNIGHT, R. G. NISLE and D. A. MILLSAY, in U.S. Atomic Energy Comm. Rept. TID-7560 (1958).
7. T. I. TAYLOR, R. H. ANDERSON and W. W. HAVENS, Jr., *Science*, **114**, 341 (1951).

8. T. I. TAYLOR and W. W. HAVENS, Jr., in, W. G. BERL (Ed.), *Physical Methods in Chemical Analysis*, Vol. 3, Academic Press, New York (1956).
9. D. J. HUGHES, *Pile Neutron Research*, Addison-Wesley, Cambridge, Mass. (1953).
10. W. KÜHN, *Atompraxis*, **5**, 133 (1959).
11. C. H. M. van BAVEL, *J. Geophys. Research*, **66**, 4193 (1961).
12. H. A. BURLEY, A. D. BLOCK and M. J. DIAMOND, *General Motors Eng. J.*, **8**, No. 1 (1961).
13. S. RUBIN, *Nuclear Instr. and Meth.*, **5**, 177 (1959).
14. R. S. ROCHLIN and W. W. SCHULTZ, *Radioisotopes for Industry*, Reinhold, New York (1959).
15. S. JEFFERSON, *Radioisotopes, A New Tool for Industry*, Newnes, London (1957).

CHAPTER 8

ISOTOPE DILUTION AND TRACER INVESTIGATIONS OF ANALYTICAL TECHNIQUES

ISOTOPE DILUTION

THE principle of isotope dilution is based on the addition of an accurately known amount of pure constituent, having a known specific activity (activity per unit mass), to an aliquot of material containing the sought constituent. After equilibration of original material and added constituent, the desired constituent is separated from the mixture, weighed and counted. From a knowledge of the specific activities of added constituent and separated constituent, the amount of constituent in the original material can be calculated. The method does not require quantitative recovery of the constituent, which offers a great advantage where quantitative separation is time-consuming or very difficult.

The added constituent, here called the "tracer", can be a stable isotope or a radio-isotope. In the former case, it is sometimes possible to determine the tracer by neutron activation. Other techniques for the analysis of stable tracers include mass spectrometry and infrared spectroscopy.

The principles of inorganic analysis by isotope dilution have been discussed in detail by Alimarin and Bilimovich,[1] whose work should be consulted for further details and modifications of the methods presented here.

An equation for isotopic dilution analysis is readily derived on the basis of conservation of total radioactivity.

Let W_1 = weight of element in original sample
$\quad W_2$ = weight of tracer element added
$\quad W$ = weight of product recovered in isolated state (not necessarily quantitative)
$\quad A_1$ = activity of the pure recovered product
$\quad A_2$ = activity of tracer element added.

It is assumed that the activity in the mixture is derived from the added tracer, and that the decay loss is negligible, so that

$$\frac{A_2}{W_1 + W_2} = \frac{A_1}{W}$$

$$\text{or, } W_1 = \left(\frac{A_2}{A_1}\right) W - W_2$$

If the specific activity of the tracer is high so that $W_2 \ll W_1$, then the previous equation reduces simple to

$$W_1 = \left(\frac{A_2}{A_1}\right) W.$$

The accuracy of isotope dilution analysis has been discussed by Weiler.[2]

Examples are now presented to illustrate typical applications of isotope dilution to inorganic analysis; these include the determination of hydrogen in metals, fluoride in acid solution and cobalt.

Hydrogen in metals has been determined by isotope dilution with tritium.[3] Briefly, tritiated hydrogen is stored as uranium hydride and is released by heating. A known amount of tritiated hydrogen, measured by its pressure in a calibrated volume, is released to the evacuated equilibration apparatus. The test specimen is then heated for a sufficiently long time to achieve equilibrium (usually 10–20 min). The pressure and specific activity of tritiated hydrogen are measured before and after equilibration with an internal gas counter for the activity measurements. The volume of the hydrogen is then calculated from the formula:

$$x = y \left((a_1/a_2) - 1 \right)$$

where: x = volume of hydrogen in sample at room temperature
 y = volume of tritiated hydrogen added
 a_1 = initial specific activity of tritiated hydrogen
 a_2 = final specific activity of tritiated hydrogen.

Surface hydrogen is determined by difference, determining hydrogen before and after the mechanical removal of surface metal. Table 8.1 presents hydrogen data taken from the work of Evans and Herrington.[3]

TABLE 8.1. SOME RESULTS OF HYDROGEN DETERMINATIONS BY ISOTOPIC DILUTION

Metal	Equilib. temp. °C	Surface hydrogen ml cm$^{-2} \times 10^3$	Dissolved hydrogen ml 100g^{-1}
Al	620	1.01	0.45
Be	850	7.5	below detection limit
U	850	5.46	0.70

Fluoride ions in acid solution have been determined by Kudahl *t al.*[4] by a rather ingenious method, in which carrier-free F^{18} tracer is added and the solution applied to defined areas of glass, where some of the tracer is adsorbed. The adsorbed F^{18} is fixed to the glass by raising the pH of the solution after equilibrium has been attained. The radioactivity on the glass is a function of the F^{18} concentration and hence the total fluoride in the solution. The measurement of the radioactivity is performed with a Geiger–Müller counter. The sensitivity of the technique can be extended to a fraction of a ppm, using autoradiographic techniques.

Isotope dilution has been applied to the spectrophotometric determination of cobalt, where the extraction of the element in 2-nitroso-l-naphthol was shown to be incomplete in the presence of a large amount of copper.[5] By adding Co^{60} tracer and determining the recovery of tracer by gamma spectrometry, the recovery was determined and the spectrophotometric data corrected.

Isotope dilution, as commonly employed, requires a knowledge of the specific activity of the unknown material. A method, discussed by Ruzikca and Stary,[6] obviates the need for determining the specific activity, thus greatly extending the usefulness of the isotope dilution approach. The authors' technique is based on always isolating the same amount of element from two solutions, to which different amounts of radiotracer have been added. Thus, the specific activities of the two solutions can be replaced by relative activities in the following equation:

$$x = y (a_1/a_2 - 1)$$

where: x = amount of unknown element in sample
y = amount of element added
a_1 = activity of element added
a_2 = activity of final solution.

The control of the amount of element extracted is achieved b
using less organic reagent than corresponds to the stoichiometri
ratio. The technique should be applicable to a number of separa
tion techniques, but will be limited here to one example, namely
the determination of zinc with dithizone.[7]

Procedure:
   Add to 10 ml of the sample solution, containing the order o
10^{-6} g of Zn/ml and a large excess of other metals, 42.50×10^{-6}
of Zn^{65} tracer y, (tracer prepared by dilution of Zn^{65} of specifi
activity 100 mc^{-1} g). Then add 4 ml of solution I [diethanol
dithiocarbamate solution, prepared by mixing 6.0 g of diethano
lamine, 3.5 g of CS_2 and 120 ml of absolute methanol, then mixin
50 ml of this solution with 450 ml of NH_4Cl–NH_4OH buffe
(0.1 N NH_4Cl, purified twice with dithizone, pH adjusted to 7.
by addition of NH_4OH] . Adjust the pH to 7.5 to 8.5, and extrac
into 1.4 ml of 10^{-4} M dithizone solution in CCl_4. Shake for 20 min
separate the organic phase and measure the gamma activity a
of 1.00 ml of extract in a well-type scintillation counter. Simul
taneously, extract a solution containing (40 to 100) $\times 10^{-6}$ g o
Zn^{65}, 4 ml of solution I and 1.4 ml of the same dithizone solutio
as in CCl_4. Count the activity a_1 of 1.00 ml of extract as before
The amount of non-active Zn is expressed by:

$$x = y(a_1/a_2 - 1)$$

Notes: 1. All the reagents are purified by dithizone extraction.
2. Large amounts of Cu, Hg, Fe, Co, Sn, Bi, Pb, Ag, Cd, and As do not interfere
3. The average precision obtained was $\pm$ 1.0 per cent for 10^{-6} to 10^{-8} g ml^{-1}
4. The sensitivity and precision can be improved with the use of Zn^{65} of highe
specific activity.

INVESTIGATIONS OF ANALYTICAL TECHNIQUES

Radiotracers are highly useful in the evaluation of analytica
procedures. Such studies include sample preparation, ashing
distillation, sublimation, evaporation, chromatographic separation
electrodeposition, solvent extraction, precipitation, co-precipitatio
and co-crystallization.
   In principle, a known amount of tracer activity is added to the
system under investigation, steps taken to assure isotopic exchange
the appropriate chemical procedure conducted and the activity
redetermined. From a knowledge of the initial and final specific
activities, a quantitative evaluation of the procedure can be made
Addition of tracer may be by neutron activation *in situ* or by

ransfer of tracer material to the system. The approaches to the
nvestigation of an analytical technique and to employing such
a technique as an analytical tool are of course similar.

A very fine tracer study has been described by Gorsuch,[8] who
nvestigated the dry and the wet oxidation of organic and biological
materials using tracers of Cu, Ag, Zn, Cd, Hg, Fe, Co, Cr, Mo,
As, Sb, Se and Sr. Emphasis was placed on the following factors:

(1)   composition of the oxidation mixtures in wet oxidation,
(2)   temperature of oxidation,
(3)   ashing acids,
(4)   retention by the crucible,
(5)   duration of the oxidation,
(6)   losses from volatility,
(7)   formation of reaction products.

It is evident from this partial list of factors that ashing is not a
simple process but requires considerable care in order to obtain
high recovery of trace elements. The paper by Gorsuch contains
much information on the conduct of tracer experiments and is
highly recommended.

Radiochemical studies on precipitation reactions of alkaline
earth sulfates have been performed by Lieser,[9] who observed that
the precipitation takes place with the same half-life as the hetero-
geneous isotopic exchange of alkaline earth ions at the surface of
the solid sulfate, indicating that the surface reaction is the rate-
determining step.

The equilibrium ion concentrations in precipitate–exchange
reactions have been determined by radiotracer techniques by
Erdey et al.[10] Briefly, the process is expressed as:

$$LM \downarrow + N^- \rightleftarrows LN \downarrow + M^-$$

where LM = exchanger
      LN = less soluble precipitate
           (the negative signs typify charges of ions without
           regard to actual valencies).

For example, the chloride exchange in the following reaction:

$$Ag_2 C_2 O_4 \downarrow + 2 Cl^- \rightleftarrows 2 AgCl \downarrow + C_2O_4^{--}$$

may be studied with Cl^{36}, i.e.,

$$Ag_2C_2O_4 \downarrow + 2\ Cl^{36-} \rightleftarrows 2\ AgCl^{36} \downarrow + C_2O_4^{--}$$

In the following reaction, similar use is made of Ag^{110},

$$Ag_2{}^{110}C_2O_4 \downarrow + 2\ Cl^- \rightleftarrows 2\ Ag^{110}Cl \downarrow + C_2O_4^{--}$$

A known amount of appropriate radiotracer solution is use
and its activity measured in a liquid Geiger–Müller counte
before and after the reaction, to determine the change of activity
From a knowledge of the specific activity of the tracer solution
the equilibrium ion concentrations can thus be calculated.

The efficiency of each step in the analysis of micro-amounts c
beryllium in urine has been determined by Toribara and Sherman[1
by addition of Be^7 tracer to an aliquot of urine and counting th
gamma activity after each step with a dipping Geiger–Mülle
counter. The resultant information permitted selection of th
most efficient combination of techniques for the determination c
micro amounts of beryllium.

REFERENCES

1. I. P. ALIMARIN and G. N. BILIMOVICH, *Int. J. Appl. Radn. Isotopes*, **7**, 16 (1960).
2. H. WEILER, *Int. J. Appl. Radn. Isotopes*, **12**, 49 (1961).
3. C. EVANS and J. HERRINGTON, in, *Radioisotopes in the Physical Sciences an Industry*, Vol. II, pp. 309–316, International Atomic Energy Agenc Vienna (1962).
4. J. N. KUDAHL, J. H. FREMLIN and J. L. HARDWICK, in, *Radioisotopes in th Physical Sciences and Industry*, Vol. II, 317–323, International Atomi Energy Agency, Vienna (1962).
5. W. D. RALPH, Jr., T. R. SWEET and I. MENCIS, *Anal. Chem.*, **34**, 92 (1962
6. J. RŮŽIKČA and J. STARÝ, *Talanta*, **8**, 228 (1961).
7. J. RŮŽIKČA and J. STARÝ, *Talanta*, **8**, 296 (1961).
8. T. T. GORSUCH, *Analyst*, **84**, 135 (1959).
9. K. H. LIESER, *Z. Elektrochem.*, **64**, 1056 (1960).
10. L. ERDEY, D. HEGEDÜS and I. PORUBSZKY, *Talanta*, **8**, 593 (1961).
11. T. Y. TORIBARA and R. E. SHERMAN, *Anal. Chem.*, **25**, 1594 (1953).

CHAPTER 9

RADIOMETRIC MEASUREMENTS AND EXCHANGE REACTIONS

RADIOMETRIC MEASUREMENTS

ACCORDING to Driscoll et al.[1] "the essence of the radiometric method of chemical analysis is the use of a reagent, whose radioactivity has been standardized in terms of chemical equivalence."

The number of moles of a reagent, consumed in radiometric reactions, is determined by a measurement of the residual activity after completion of the reaction or by a measurement of the radioactivity of the reaction product. Driscoll et al.[1] further state that the excess activity must be in a different form from the product in order to be distinguished by counting." Such analyses can be expressed by the equation.[1]

$$Ai = D \left[\frac{n_A}{n_B} B (1 - u) \right]$$

where A_i = initial concentration of unknown,

B_i = initial concentration of radioactivity reagent,

u = ratio: activity remaining/initial activity,

D = distribution coefficient,

n_A and n_B = ions or ligands. Typical applications are now presented.

Procedure:[1a] Ion determined: soluble chloride, using Ag^{110} tracer.

Preparation of stock solutions: Use dried NaCl to prepare aqueous stock solutions ranging from 1 to 500 ppm of chloride. Weigh out dried $AgNO_3$, dissolve in 0.2 M HNO_3, add the Ag^{110} tracer to the $AgNO_3$ solution and dilute to form stock solutions ranging in total silver content from 30–2000 ppm. Pipet a 50 μl aliquot of each Ag^{110} solution into a separate 1½-dram test vial and combine three pipet rinses with the contents of the vial; dilute each vial to a 1.0 ml volume with water.

Pipet a 1.00 ml aliquot of a chloride stock solution into a 12 ml centrifuge cone. Rinse the pipet with dilute HNO_3, then with water, combining the rinses with the content of the centrifuge cone.

Using the same pipetting procedure, pipet 1.00 ml of Ag^{110} stoc solution into the same centrifuge cone. Place the cone in a constan temperature bath and stir the contents for 3 min with ultrasonic o mechanical agitation. Centrifuge and then pipet 50 μl of th supernate into a 1½-dram vial. Dilute to 1.0 ml. Place the standar Ag^{110} vial and later the test vial, into the well of the gamm scintillation spectrometer, adjusted to measure the 0.66 and 0.8 MeV gamma rays from Ag^{110}. By a comparison of the countin rates and correcting for dilutions, calculate the silver content o the supernate. From the initial and final silver concentrations calculate the chloride content of the solution.

Procedure:[2] *Element determined: dissolved oxygen in water.*
    Reaction: 4 Tl(s) + O_2(aq) + 2 H_2O (liq) ——▶ 4 Tl^+(aq) + 4 OH^- (aq).
    Electroplate approximately one gram of Tl^{204}-labeled Tl on t copper turnings, bring the Tl in contact with the water sample, an determine the Tl activity of a sample of the water solution afte allowing sufficient time for completion of the reaction. From th counting data, calculate the dissolved oxygen content of the wate sample.

Notes: 1. With Tl^{204} of specific activity 2 mcg^{-1}, a limit of detection of 0.2 ppr was attained; undiluted Tl^{204}, as furnished by Oak Ridge National Laboratory would increase the sensitivity to a limit of detection of about 0.1 ppb.
2. Salt water and sea water gave a non-linear response above 3 ppm, necessitatin the use of a calibration curve.
3. Generally licensed quantities of Tl^{204}, 50 μc, will set a lower limit of abou 1 ppm.

EXCHANGE REACTIONS

Non-radioactive material at trace concentrations has bee determined by exchanging the non-radioactive material for a measurable radio-isotope. This technique has found application i the measurement of strong oxidizing gases such as fluorine, ozone nitrogen dioxide and in the measurement of active hydrogen i chemical compounds.

In many cases, Kr^{85}-labeled krypton quinol clathrate is em ployed and the released Kr^{85} determined; the chemistry of the solic clathrates has been described by Powell.[3-4] In the analysis o weaker oxidizing gases, it is possible to react the gas with a soli agent to release a stronger oxidizing gas. For example, Chleck and Ziegler[5] have described the use of the following reactions fo air pollution studies:

$$SO_2(g) + ClO_2^- \text{ (solid) } \longrightarrow ClO_2(g)$$
$$ClO_2(g) + 3 \text{ quinol.}Kr^{85} \text{ (solid) } \longrightarrow Kr^{85} \text{ (g)},$$

here the second reaction represents the release of the radio-isotopes. he technique permits the determination of oxidizing gases of quantity as small as 10^{-14}g.

The analysis of active hydrogen in organic compounds has een performed with the aid of tritium-labeled $LiAlH_4$. Chleck t al.[6] have determined active hydrogen by this method in n-utanol, benzoic acid, aniline and water by reacting 0.2 M $LiAlH_4$[3] specific activity (5–20) × 10^{-4} mc/millimole)) in diethyl carbitol vith the sample; evolved tritium was counted with a windowless as-flow proportional counter. After corrections for background nd volume, the counting rate is proportional to the concentration f the active hydrogen.

Surface area of powdered materials can be determined by two adiotracer methods:

(1) surface exchange.
(2) gas adsorption.

The surface exchange method for the determination of the urface area of UO_2 powder has been reported by Ferguson and eddicotte.[7] The method is based on the exchange reaction be-ween non-radioactive ions on the surface of an insoluble solid nd radioactive ions of the same species in saturated solution. Thus, saturated solution containing U^{237} tracer (half-life 6.75 days), n contact with UO_2 powder (assumed to be relatively non-radio-ctive) is agitated and the change in radioactivity of the solution bserved. The initial rapid decrease in solution activity is ascribed o the exchange reaction. The amount of U^{237} tracer removed rom the solution by exchange is a measure of the surface area of he solid. In a typical run, the surface area of UO_2 powder was etermined as 1.5×10^3 cm^2 g^{-1}.[7]

The adsorption of a radioactive gas, such as Kr^{85}, has been used to determine the surface area of solids such as iron oxide,[8] .g., by the BET technique.[9]

REFERENCES

1. W. J. DRISCOLL, B. F. SCOTT and E. A. HUFF, U.S. Atomic Energy Comm. Rept. TID–11306 (1961).
1a. Modified version of above report, as modified by A. J. MOSES.
2. H. G. RICHTER and A. S. GILLESPIE, Jr., *Anal. Chem.*, **34**, 1116 (1962).

3. H. M. POWELL, *J. Chem. Soc.*, **1950**, 298, 300, 468.
4. H. M. POWELL and M. GUTER, *Nature*, **164**, 240 (1949).
5. D. J. CHLECK and C. A. ZIEGLER, in, *Radioisotopes in the Physical Science and Industry*, Vol. II, 351–360, International Atomic Energy Agency Vienna (1962).
6. D. J. CHLECK, F. BROUSAIDES, W. SULLIVAN and C. A. ZIEGLER, *Int. Appl. Radn. Isotopes*, **7**, 182 (1960).
7. R. L. FERGUSON and G. W. LEDDICOTTE, U.S. Atomic Energy Comm. Rep ORNL–CF–59–8–62 (1959).
8. W. AYLMORE and W. B. JEPSON, *J. Sci. Instr.*, **38**, 156 (1961).
9. S. BRUNAUER, P. H. EMMETT and E. TELLER, *J. Am. Chem. Soc.*, **60**, 30 (1938).

CHAPTER 10

GEO- AND COSMOCHRONOLOGY AND MISCELLANEOUS NUCLEAR TECHNIQUES

GEO- AND COSMOCHRONOLOGY

DECAY of radioactivity of known half-life can be used for dating minerals, waters, carbonaceous materials etc. The discussion here will deal with (1) natural radioactivity and (2) cosmic-ray induced radioactivity. Table 10.1 provides information on some natural radioactivities of interest in geological dating.

TABLE 10.1. HALF-LIVES OF SOME NUCLIDES OF IMPORTANCE IN GEOLOGICAL DATING [1[

Parent nuclide	End product	Type of decay	Half-life, years
U^{235}	Pb^{207}	α	7.13×10^8
U^{238}	Pb^{206}	α	4.49×10^9
Th^{232}	Pb^{208}	α	1.39×10^{10}
Rb^{87}	Sr^{87}	$\beta-$	4.7×10^{10}
K^{40}	Ca^{40}	$\beta-$	$1.46 \times 10^{9}*$
	Ar^{40}	K capture	$1.19 \times 10^{10}*$
Lu^{176}	Hf^{176}	$\beta-$	7.3×10^{10}
Re^{187}	Os^{187}	$\beta-$	$\sim 10^{11}$

*The average half-life of K^{40} 1.28×10^9 years, using a branching ratio of 0.123.

Measurements with lead isotopic are based on the assumption that U^{235} and U^{238} were formed in equal abundance but decayed at different rates [1-4]. Similar assumptions are made in the case of the isotopes of other elements. Because the final lead isotopes are stable, the decay of the U^{238} chain is analyzed radiochemically by assaying the Pb^{210} isotope (22 year half-life), which is in equilibrium with U^{238} in older ores. In actual practice, Pb^{210} is best analyzed by α-counting its Po^{210} daughter.

Alpha decay in the U^{235}, U^{238} and Th^{232} series leads to the formation of helium. Measurement of the He can then be used to determine the age of the mineral. This technique assumed initial absence of He, no retentivity of He in rock, no addition of He from other radioactive parents such as Sm^{147}, and no loss of He from leakage. For such reasons, the He method is not considered as reliable as the lead methods.

Neutrons are produced by the interaction of high energy cosmic radiation with the atmosphere. These neutrons react with atmospheric gases and produce activities such as H^3, Be^7, Be^{10} and C^{14}. In addition to this mode of production, radioactivity is released to the atmosphere by nuclear weapons tests and by gaseous decay products from uranium- and thorium-bearing ores. H^3, Be^7 and Be^{10} have been used as "natural" tracers for the study of meteorological phenomena. Be^{10} may become incorporated in deep sea sediments and serve as a means for dating these sediments. Atmospheric activities and related dating procedures have been discussed in detail by Maddock and Willis.[5]

The analytical chemist usually refers to the C^{14} technique in "age dating." C^{14} is formed as a result of the interaction of cosmic ray-produced neutrons with nitrogen in the atmosphere, as indicated by the reaction: N^{14} (n, p) C^{14}. The thermal activation cross section for this reaction is 1.75 barns and the half-life of C^{14} is 5568 ± 30 years. C^{14} decays by emission of a beta particle with a maximum energy of 0.155 MeV. The newly formed C^{14} atoms are oxidized in the atmosphere to $C^{14}O_2$ and complete mixing then takes place between $C^{14}O_2$ and CO_2.[6] The specific activity of carbon in the biosphere is 16 disintegrations/min/g.[7] When an animal or a plant dies, its assimilation of carbon ceases and its C^{14} content decays. The C^{14} dating method assumes the specific activity of carbon has remained unchanged through the ages. (This is not strictly correct today, owing to increased combustion of fossil fuels and the conduct of atmospheric nuclear explosions.) Thus, if a specimen from a tree shows a specific carbon activity of 8 disintegrations min^{-1} g^{-1} today, this is interpreted to mean that the tree was formed 5568 years ago. With present analytical techniques, the limiting age of specimens for C^{14} dating is about 50,000 years.

The C^{14} dating technique has been pioneered by Libby,[6] who developed a special type of internal Geiger–Müller counter, the "screen wall counter," for counting elemental carbon. Carbon was prepared from the specimens by a thorough purification procedure in which carbon was converted to CO_2 and then to elemental carbon. Recently, a simplified procedure has been developed in which CO_2 is converted to methane by a one-step catalytic hydrogenation using a ruthenium catalyst for subsequent counting of methane.[8] Fig. 10.1 shows a commercially available C^{14} dating apparatus, including sample preparation and counting devices. The apparatus is based on conversion to methane.

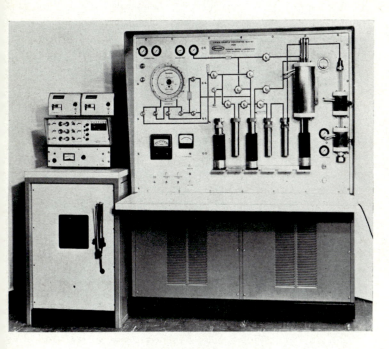

FIG. 10.1 C^{14} dating laboratory
(Courtesy of Sharp Laboratories, Inc., La Jolla, Calif.)

MISCELLANEOUS NUCLEAR TECHNIQUES

A number of specialized nuclear techniques are of interest to the analytical chemist, but are not sufficiently broad in application to permit detailed treatment in this monograph. Therefore, these techniques will only be briefly presented but documented with adequate references.

The analysis by photon- or particle-induced reactions is, of course, related to the isotopic composition of the target. Therefore, any of these reactions serve to establish the concentration of at least one of the isotopes of the target material. One example is the thermal-neutron induced fission of uranium, where U^{235} is the fissionable isotope.

The burnup analysis of fissionable isotopes has recently received adequate attention by Rider and Ruiz.[9]

The analysis of Li^6 by successive nuclear reactions is a recently announced technique of considerable interest.[10] Briefly, a lithium sample was exposed to a thermal neutron flux of 1×10^{13} n cm^{-2} sec^{-1}, resulting in the following two successive reactions:

$$Li^6(n, \alpha)H^3$$
$$O^{18}(H^3, \alpha)N^{17}.$$

The delayed neutrons, emitted by N^{17}, were counted by Amiel and Welwart;[10] the maximum sensitivity was obtained by dissolving the sample in O^{18}—enriched water prior to the irradiation. Amiel[11] has used a similar technique for the determination of fissionable isotopes of U, Th and Pu, measuring delayed neutrons from fission products. This technique was further investigated by Dyer et al.[12] for the analysis of large numbers of samples for U^{235}. This neutron activation-delayed neutron counting technique is capable of determining as little as 10^{-9} μg of U^{235}[13]

Oxygen has been analyzed by activation with tritons formed by neutron bombardment of lithium, The reactions are:

$$Li^6(n, \alpha)H^3$$
$$O^{16}(H^3, n) F^{18}.$$

F^{18} decays with a half-life of 1.87 hr with positron emission. Born and Wilkniss[13] have determined the capability of the method to extend down to 0.01 ppm of oxygen, using appropriate procedures to separate F^{18} from the matrix material.

Deuterium in heavy water has been analyzed by the reaction O^{16} (d, n) F^{17}, where the deuterons were produced by (n, d) collisions.[14] The resultant F^{17} activity was shown to be proportional to the H^2 concentration of the water. A reactor flux of 10^{12} thermal n/cm^2/sec provided the means of activation.

Sometimes it is difficult to ascertain the concentration of impurities in materials by the techniques previously cited. In such cases, an isotopically-labeled impurity may be introduced and its distribution in the material observed. A typical example of such a use of radiotracers is the determination of phosphorus in silicon iodide, an intermediate in the preparation of transistor-grade silicon by zone refining.[15] With P^{32} tracer, it was possible to determine the distribution of phosphorus after three passes of the molten zone (see Fig. 10.2).

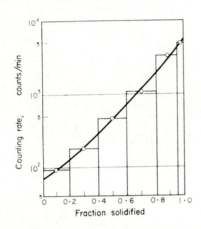

FIG. 10.2.   Distribution of phosphorus after three passes of molten zone[15]

REFERENCES

1. A. A. SMALES and L. R. WAGER, *Methods in Geochemistry*, Interscience, New York (1960).
2. R. D. RUSSELL and R. M. FARQUHAR, *Lead Isotopes in Geology*, Interscience, New York (1960).
3. K. RANKAMA, *Isotope Geology*, Pergamon Press, London (1954).
4. *Nuclear Processes in Geologic Settings*, Publ. 400, National Academy of Sciences—National Research Council, Washington, 1956.
5. A. G. MADDOCK and E. H. WILLIS, in *Advances in Inorganic Chemistry and Radiochemistry*, H. J. EMELÉUS and A. G. SHARPE, (Eds.), Academic Press, New York, Vol. 3 (1961).
6. W. F. LIBBY, *Radiocarbon Dating*, Univ. Chicago Press, Chicago (1952).
7. H. OESCHGER, *Schweizer Archiv*, **28**, 55 (1962).

8. A. W. FAIRHALL, W. R. SCHELL and Y. TAKASHIMA, *Rev. Sci. Instr.*, **32**, 323 (1961).
9. B. F. RIDER and C. P. RUIZ, *The Determination of Atom Per Cent Fission in Uranium Fuel* in Progress in Nuclear Energy, Series IX, Vol. 3, 1–3, Analytical Chemistry, C. E. CROUTHAMEL, Ed., Pergamon Press, The Macmillan Company, New York (1962).
10. S. AMIEL and Y. WELWART, Israel Atomic Energy Comm. Rept. IA-690 (1962).
11. S. AMIEL, *Anal. Chem.*, **34**, 1963 (1962).
12. F. F. DYER, J. F. EMERY and G. W. LEDDICOTTE, U.S. Atomic Energy Comm. Rept. ORNL-3342 (1962).
13. H. J. BORN and P. WILKNISS, *Int. J. Appl. Radn. Isotopes*, **10**, 133 (1961).
14. S. AMIEL and M. PEISACH, *Anal. Chem.*, **34**, 1305 (1962).
15. H. BABA, T. NOZAKI and H. ARAKI, *Bull. Chem. Soc. Japan*, **32**, 537 (1959).

CHART OF THE NUCLIDES

(Reprinted by permission of the Knolls Atomic Power Laboratory, operated by the General Electric Company under direction of the Naval Reactors Branch, U.S. Atomic Energy Commission.)

MONOGRAPHS ON THE RADIOCHEMISTRY OF THE ELEMENTS

THE following monographs on the radiochemistry of the elements have been prepared by the U.S. National Research Council in co-operation with other Government agencies. The reports are available in the United States of America from the Office of Technical Services, U.S. Department of Commerce, Washington 25, D.C. at the prices shown.

NAS–NS–3001	The Radiochemistry of Cadmium; De Voe	$0.75
NAS–NS–3002	The Radiochemistry of Arsenic; Beard	0.50
NAS–NS–3003	The Radiochemistry of Francium; Hyde	0.50
NAS–NS–3004	The Radiochemistry of Thorium; Hyde	0.75
NAS–NS–3005	The Radiochemistry of Fluorine, Chlorine, Bromine and Iodine; Kleinberg and Cowan	0.50
NAS–NS–3006	The Radiochemistry of Americium and Curium; Penneman and Keenan	0.75
NAS–NS–3007	The Radiochemistry of Chromium; Piijck	0.50
NAS–NS–3008	The Radiochemistry of Rhodium; Choppin	0.50
NAS–NS–3009	The Radiochemistry of Molybdenum; Scadden and Ballou	0.50
NAS–NS–3010	The Radiochemistry of Barium, Calcium and Strontium; Sunderman and Townley	1.25
NAS–NS–3011	The Radiochemistry of Zirconium and Hafnium; Steinberg	0.50
NAS–NS–3012	The Radiochemistry of Astatine; Appleman	0.50
NAS–NS–3013	The Radiochemistry of Beryllium; Fairhall	0.50
NAS–NS–3014	The Radiochemistry of Indium; Sunderman and Townley	0.50
NAS–NS–3015	The Radiochemistry of Zinc; Hicks	0.75
NAS–NS–3016	The Radiochemistry of Protactinium; Kirby	1.00
NAS–NS–3017	The Radiochemistry of Iron; Nielsen	0.50
NAS–NS–3018	The Radiochemistry of Manganese; Leddicotte	0.50
NAS–NS–3019	The Radiochemistry of Carbon, Nitrogen and Oxygen; Hudis	0.50
NAS–NS–3020	The Radiochemistry of the Rare Earths, Scandium, Yttrium and Actinium; Stevenson and Nervik	3.00
NAS–NS–3021	The Radiochemistry of Technetium; Anders	0.50
NAS–NS–3022	The Radiochemistry of Vanadium; Brownlee	0.75
NAS–NS–3023	The Radiochemistry of Tin; Nervik	0.75

NAS–NS–3024	The Radiochemistry of Magnesium; Fairhall	$0.50
NAS–NS–3025	The Radiochemistry of the Rare Gases; Momyer	0.75
NAS–NS–3026	The Radiochemistry of Mercury; Roesmer and Kruger	0.50
NAS–NS–3027	The Radiochemistry of Copper; Dyer and Leddicotte	0.75
NAS–NS–3028	The Radiochemistry of Rhenium; Leddicotte	0.50
NAS–NS–3029	The Radiochemistry of Ruthenium; Wyatt and Rickard	1.00
NAS–NS–3030	The Radiochemistry of Selenium; Leddicotte	0.50
NAS–NS–3031	The Radiochemistry of the Transcurium Elements; Higgins	0.50
NAS–NS–3032	The Radiochemistry of Aluminum and Gallium; Lewis	0.50
NAS–NS–3033	The Radiochemistry of Antimony; Maeck	0.50
NAS–NS–3034	The Radiochemistry of Titanium; Kim	0.50
NAS–NS–3035	The Radiochemistry of Cesium; Finston and Kinsley	0.75
NAS–NS–3036	The Radiochemistry of Gold; Emery and Leddicotte	0.50
NAS–NS–3037	The Radiochemistry of Polinium; Figgins	0.75
NAS–NS–3038	The Radiochemistry of Tellurium; Leddicotte	0.50
NAS–NS–3039	The Radiochemistry of Niobium and Tantalum; Steinberg	0.75
NAS–NS–3040	The Radiochemistry of Lead; Gibson	1.75
NAS–NS–3041	The Radiochemistry of Cobalt; Bate and Leddicotte	1.00
NAS–NS–3042	The Radiochemistry of Tungsten; Mullins and Leddicotte	0.50
NAS–NS–3043	The Radiochemistry of Germanium; Marinsky	0.50
NAS–NS–3044	The Radiochemistry of Platinum; Leddicotte	0.50
NAS–NS–3045	The Radiochemistry of Iridium; Leddicotte	0.50
NAS–NS–3046	The Radiochemistry of Osmium; Leddicotte	0.50
NAS–NS–3047	The Radiochemistry of Silver; Sunderman and Townley	0.75
NAS–NS–3048	The Radiochemistry of Potassium; Mullins and Leddicotte	0.50
NAS–NS–3049	The Radiochemistry of Silicon; Mullins and Leddicotte	0.50
NAS–NS–3050	The Radiochemistry of Uranium, Parts I and II; Glinder	3.50
NAS–NS–3051	The Radiochemistry of Nickel; Kirby	3.50
NAS–NS–3052	The Radiochemistry of Palladium; Hogdahl	0.75
NAS–NS–3053	The Radiochemistry of Rubidium; Leddicotte	0.50
NAS–NS–3054	The Radiochemistry of Sulfur; Leddicotte	0.50
NAS–NS–3055	The Radiochemistry of Sodium; Mullins and Leddicotte	0.50
NAS–NS–3056	The Radiochemistry of Phosphorus	0.50

Following is a list of monographs on radiochemical techniques, issued in conjunction with the preceding series.

| NAS–NS–3101 | Liquid–Liquid Extraction with High Molecular Weight Amines; Moore | 1.00 |
| NAS–NS–3102 | Separation by Extraction with Tri-*n*-octyl phosphine oxide; White and Ross | 0.75 |

NAS–NS–3103	Low Level Radiochemistry; Sugihara	$0.50
NAS–NS–3104	Rapid Radiochemical Separations; Kusaka and Meinke	1.25
NAS–NS–3105	Detection and Measurement of Nuclear Radiation; G. D. O'Kelley	1.50

URANIUM AND THORIUM STANDARDS

1. Counting standards, available from New Brunswick Laboratory, U.S. Atomic Energy Commission, New Brunswick, New Jersey.

A set of four ore samples for calibrating counting equipment is available at $10.00/set, containing pitchblende with 4.0, 2.0, 1.0 and 0.5 per cent U. Additional powdered ores of various U and Th content are available from the same supplier. A complete list is provided in the author's text on actinides.*

2. Isotopic uranium standards are available from the U.S. National Bureau of Standards, Washington 25, D.C. These standards comprise:
   (a) natural uranium, sample No. 950, 25 g U_3O_8, $5.00.
   (b) enriched uranium, nominal U^{245} content: 0.5, 1, 1.5, 2, 3, 5, 20, 85, 90, 93 wt. per cent, price ranging from $20 to $38 per 1 g of U_3O_8.

*A. J. MOSES, *Analytical Chemistry of the Actinide Elements*, Pergamon Press, The Macmillan Co., New York (1963).

APPENDIX D

Product Nuclide	Half-life	Isotopic σ_{ac}, barns	Isotopic abundance, %	Decay modes	Maximum Beta Ray energy, Me
Na–24	14.97 hr	0.51	100	β^-	1.39
Mg–27	9.45 min	0.026	11.1	β^-	1.57, 1.75
Al–28	2.30 min	0.21	100	β^-	2.87
Si–31	2.62 hr	0.094	3.12	β^-	1.48
P–32	14.6 days	0.191	100	β^-	1.71
S–35	87.1 days	0.26	4.22	β^-	0.167
Cl–38	37.3 min	0.56	24.6	β^-	1.1, 2.8, 4.8
Ar–41	1.83 hr	0.53	99.60	β^+	1.20
K–42	12.4 hr	1.0	6.91	β^-	1.97, 3.55
Ca–45	160 days	0.63	2.06	β^-	0.25
Ca–49	8.7 min	1.1	0.185	β^-	0.89, 2.0
Sc–46	83.9 days	22	100	β^-	0.36
Ti–51	5.79 min	0.14	5.34	β^-	1.52, 2.13
V–52	3.77 min	4.5	99.75	β^-	2.6
Cr–51	27.8 days	13.5	4.31	E C	—
Mn–56	2.58 hr	13.4	100	β^-	0.75, 1.05, 2.
Fe–59	45 days	0.9	0.31	β^-	0.27, 0.46, 1.
Co–60m	10.47 min	16	100	IT, β^-	1.54
Co–60	5.27 years	36	100	β^-	0.31, 1.48
Ni–65	2.56 hr	1.6	1.16	β^-	0.6, 1.0, 2.1
Cu–64	12.9 hr	3.62	69.1	EC, β^-, β^+	β^-0.57, β^+0.(
Cu–66	5.1 min	1.8	30.9	β^-	1.59, 2.63
Zn–65	245 days	0.5	48.9	EC, β^+	β^+ 0.33
Ga–70	20.2 min	1.4	60.2	β^-	1.65
Ga–72	14.3 hr	5.0	39.8	β^-	0.64, 0.96
Ge–71	11.4 days	3.9	20.55	EC	
Ge–75	1.4 hr	0.22	36.7	β^-	0.92, 1.18
Ge–77	11 hr	0.080	7.67	β^-	0.71, 1.38, 2.2
As–76	26.5 hr	4.2	100	β^-	1.76, 2.41, 2.
Se–75	120 days	26	0.87	EC	—
Se–81	18 min	0.5	49.82	β^-	1.38
Se–83	25 min	0.004	9.19	β^-	0.45, 1.0, 1.7
Br–80	18 min	8.5	50.52	EC, β^-, β^+	β^-1.38, 2.00,β^+
Br–80m	4.58 hr	2.9	50.52	IT, CE	—
Br–82	1.50 days	3.5	49.48	β^-	0.44
Kr–79	1.4 days	2	0.354	EC, β^+	β^+ 0.60

ominent photon energies and their abundance per 100 Beta isintegrations, energies in MeV	Saturation activity,* dpm/μg of element	Specific activity,* 1 hr irradiation, dpm/μg of element
7 (100) 2.75 (100)	8.0×10^5	4.0×10^4
4 (70) 1.02 (30)	4.4×10^3	4.4×10^3
5 (100)	3.0×10^5	3.0×10^5
5 (0.07)	3.8×10^3	8.8×10^2
e	2.2×10^5	4.8×10^2
e	1.2×10^4	4.2
) (31) 2.15 (47)	1.4×10^5	1.0×10^5
9 (99)	4.8×10^5	1.6×10^5
3 (18)	6.4×10^4	3.8×10^3
e	1.1×10^4	2.1
) (89) 4.05 (8) 4.68 (3)	1.8×10^3	1.8×10^3
9 (100) 1.12 (100)	1.7×10^7	4.4×10^3
2 (96) 0.61 (1) 0.93 (4)	5.6×10^3	5.6×10^3
4 (100)	3.2×10^6	3.2×10^6
2 (10)	4.0×10^5	4.0×10^2
2 (99) 1.77 (23) 2.06 (14)	8.8×10^6	2.2×10^6
) (56) 1.29 (44)	1.8×10^3	1.3
59 (99.7) 1.33 (0.3)	9.8×10^6	9.8×10^6
73 (100) 1.333 (100)	2.2×10^7	3.2×10^2
7 (3) 1.12 (10) 1.49 (20)	1.1×10^4	2.8×10^3
4 (1) 0.51 (AN)	1.4×10^6	8.1×10^4
4 (9)	3.1×10^5	3.1×10^5
2 (50) 0.51 (AN)	1.3×10^5	1.6×10^1
4 (1)	4.4×10^5	3.9×10^5
3 (19) 0.83 (88) 2.20 (29)	1.0×10^6	5.2×10^4
e	4.1×10^5	1.1×10^3
6 (11)	4.0×10^4	1.6×10^4
68 0.418 0.564	3.0×10^3	2.0×10^2
5 (45) 0.66 (6) 1.21 (6)	2.0×10^6	5.4×10^4
2 (15) 0.14 (54) 0.27 (56) 0.28 (23)	1.0×10^5	2.6×10^1
e	1.1×10^5	1.0×10^5
5	1.8×10^2	1.5×10^2
2 (13) 0.51 (AN)	1.9×10^6	1.7×10^6
37 (100) 0.049 (100)	6.6×10^5	1.1×10^5
5 (64) 0.77 (80) 1.03 (26)	7.8×10^5	1.6×10^4
45 0.084 0.136	3.2×10^3	7.0×10^1

Product Nuclide	Half-life	Isotopic σ_{ac}, barns	Isotopic Abundance, %	Decay modes	Maximum Beta Ray energy, Me
Kr–85m	4.36 hr	0.10	56.90	IT, CE, β^-	0.83
Kr–87	1.3 hr	0.060	17.37	β^-	1.3, 3.3 3.
Rb–86	19.5 days	0.80	72.15	β^-	0.7, 1.77
Rb–88	17.8 min	0.12	27.85	β^-	0.33, 2.0, 5.2
Sr–85m	1.2 hr	<1	0.56	IT, CE, EC	—
Sr–85	65 days	1.0	0.56	EC	—
Sr–87m	2.8 hr	1.3	9.86	IT, CE	—
Sr–89	53 days	0.005	82.56	β^-	1.46
Y–90	2.7 days	1.26	100	β^-	2.27
Zr–95	65 days	0.09	17.40	β^-	0.36, 0.40
Zr–97	17 hr	0.10	2.80	β^-	1.27, 1.91
Nb–94m	6.6 min	1.0	100	IT, CE	—
Mo–99	2.75 days	0.45	23.75	β^-	0.41, 0.80, 1.
Ru–97	2.88 days	0.21	5.57	EC, CE	—
Ru–103	40 days	1.44	31.5	β^-	0.12, 0.22
Ru–105	4.44 hr	0.7	18.5	β^-	1.18
Rh–104m	4.4 min	12	100	IT	—
Pd–103	17 days	4.8	0.80	EC, CE	—
Pd–109m	4.8 min	0.07	26.7	IT, CE	—
Pd–109	13.6 hr	12	26.7	β^-, CE	1.0
Pd–111	22 min	0.4	13.5	β^-	2.13
Pd–111m	5.5 hr	0.02	13.5	IT, CE	—
Ag–108	2.4 min	45	51.35	β^-	1.77
Ag–110m	253 days	3.2	48.65	β^-, IT	0.086, 0.54
Cd–107	6.7 hr	1.0	1.22	β^+, EC	0.32
Cd–109	1.3 years		0.88	EC, CE	—
Cd–111m	48.6 min	0.2	12.39	IT, CE	—
Cd–113m	5.1 years	0.03	24.07	β^-	0.59
Cd–115m	44 days	0.14	28.86	β^-	0.69, 1.63
Cd–115	2.3 days	1.1	28.8	β^-	0.59, 1.11
Cd–117m	2.9 hr	1.5	7.58	β^-	1.0
Cd–117	50 min		7.58	β^-	1.5
In–114m	50 days	56	4.23	IT, EC, CE	—
In–116m	54.0 min	155	95.77	β^-	0.60, 0.85, 1.
Sn–113	119 days	1.3	0.95	EC, CE	—
Sn–117m	14 days	0.006	14.24	IT, CE	—
Sn–119m	245 days	0.01	24.01	IT, CE	—
Sn–121m	>5 years	0.001	32.97	β^-	0.42
Sn–121	1.12 days	0.14	32.97	β^-	0.38
Sn–123	40 min	0.16	4.71	β^-	1.26
Sn–123m	130 days	0.001	4.71	β^-	1.42
Sn–125	9.5 min	0.2	5.98	β^-	2.04
Sn–125m	10 days	0.004	5.98	β^-	2.35
Sb–122m	3.5 min	0.19	57.25	IT	—
Sb–122	2.8 days	6.8	57.25	β^-, EC	1.40, 1.97
Sb–124m[1]	1.3 min	0.03	42.75	β^-, IT, CE	3.2
Sb–124m[2]	21 min	0.03	42.75	β^-, IT	3

Prominent photon energies and their abundance per 100 Beta disintegrations, energies in MeV	Saturation activity,* dpm/μg of element	Specific activity,* 1 hour irradiation, dpm/μg of element
15 (74) 0.31 (22)	2.5×10^4	3.9×10^3
40 (75) 0.85 (5) 2.57 (25)	4.5×10^3	1.9×10^3
08 (9)	2.4×10^5	3.8×10^2
90 (9) 1.86 (15)	1.4×10^4	1.3×10^4
008 (13) 0.150 (86) 0.225 (13)	$<2.4 \times 10^3$	$<1.1 \times 10^3$
51 (100)	2.3×10^3	1.0
39 (100)	5.3×10^4	1.2×10^4
ne	1.7×10^3	1.0
ne	5.1×10^5	5.6×10^3
72 (55) 0.76 (43) 0.77 (99)*	6.2×10^3	2.9
75 (96)*	1.1×10^3	4.8×10^1
041 (100)	3.9×10^5	3.9×10^5
140 (80) 0.74 (11)	4.0×10^4	4.4×10^2
109 0.325 (6) 0.216 (94)	4.2×10^3	4.4×10^1
040 (96)* 0.498 (90) 0.610 (7)	1.6×10^5	1.3×10^2
30 (100)* 0.72 (100)	4.7×10^4	7.1×10^3
051 (100) 0.077 (100)	4.3×10^6	4.3×10^6
040 (100)* 0.30 (1) 0.50 (1)	1.3×10^4	2.6×10^1
18 (100)	6.5×10^3	6.5×10^3
988 (100)* 0.30	1.1×10^6	4.6×10^4
07 (100)*	1.8×10^4	1.6×10^4
47 (75)	9.2×10^2	1.2×10^2
43 (0.2) 0.63 (1)	7.7×10^6	7.7×10^6
56 (100) 0.88 (80)	5.4×10^5	6.5×10^1
994 (0.4)* 0.85 (0.4)	4.0×10^3	4.4×10^2
088 (100)*		
50 (100) 0.247 (100)	8.0×10^3	4.8×10^3
27 (0.1)	2.4×10^3	<1
4 (2) 1.29 (1)	1.3×10^4	1.2×10^1
35 (95)*	1.0×10^5	1.3×10^3
27 0.43	3.8×10^4	8.4×10^3
2		
92 (19) 0.56 (4) 0.72 (4)	7.4×10^5	4.6×10^2
1 (25) 1.08 (54) 1.27 (75)	4.7×10^7	2.5×10^7
255 (2) 0.39 (100)*	3.7×10^3	<1
59 (100) 0.161 (100)	2.6×10^2	<1
024 (100) 0.065 100)	7.5×10^2	<1
ne	$<1 \times 10^2$	<1
ne	1.4×10^4	3.9×10^2
6 (100)	2.3×10^3	1.6×10^3
8 (2)	1.5×10^1	<1
3 (99) 1.07 (4) 1.39 (2)	3.7×10^3	3.7×10^3
7 (4) 1.97 (1)	7.6×10^1	<1
61 (100) 0.075 (100)	3.2×10^4	3.2×10^4
6 (66) 0.69 (3) 1.14 (1)	1.2×10^6	1.3×10^4
12	4.0×10^3	4.0×10^3
18	4.0×10^3	3.6×10^3

Product Nuclide	Half-life		Isotopic σ_{ac}, barns	Isotopic Abundance, %	Decay modes	Maximum Beta Ray energy, MeV
Sb–124	60	days	2.5	42.75	β^-	0.22, 0.61, 2.3
Te–121m	150	days		0.089	IT, CE	—
Te–121	17	days		0.089	EC	—
Te–123m	104	days	1.1	2.46	IT, CE	—
Te–125m	58	days	5	4.61	IT	—
Te–127m	105	days	0.09	18.71	β^-, IT	0.73
Te–127	9.4	hr	0.15	18.71	β^-	0.70
Te–129m	33	days	0.015	31.79	IT, CE	—
Te–129	1.1	hr	0.13	31.79	β^-	1.00, 1.45
Te–131m	1.2	days	<0.008	34.49	β^-, IT, CE	0.42, 0.57, 2.47
Te–131	25	min	0.22	34.49	β^-	1.69, 2.14
I–128	25.0	min	5.6	100	β^-, EC	1.67, 2.12
Xe–125	18	hr	74	0.096	EC	—
Xe–127	36.4	days		0.090	EC	—
Xe–129m	8.0	days	<5	1.919	IT, CE	—
Xe–131m	12	days	<5	4.08	IT, CE	—
Xe–133m	2.3	days	<5	26.89	IT, CE	—
Xe–133	5.27	days	0.2	26.89	β^-, CE	—
Xe–135m	15.6	min	<0.5	10.44	IT, CE	—
Xe–135	9.2	hr	0.2	10.44	β^-	0.55, 0.91
Xe–137	3.9	min	0.15	8.87	β^-	3.5
Cs–134m	3.1	hr	0.017	100	β^-, IT, CE	0.55
Cs–134	2.3	years	30	100	β^-	0.09, 0.65
Ba–131	11.6	days	10	0.101	EC	—
Ba–133m	1.63	days	7	0.097	IT, CE	—
Ba–133	7.2	years	7	0.097	EC	—
Ba–135m	1.21	days	2	2.42	IT, CE	—
Ba–137m	2.60	min	0.5	7.81	IT, CE	—
Ba–139	1.42	hr	0.5	71.66	β^-	2.38
La–140	40.2	hr	8.2	99.91	β^-	2.20
Ce–137m	34	hr	0.6	0.193	IT, CE	—
Ce–137	8.7	hr	6.3	0.193	EC, CE	—
Ce–139	140	days	0.6	0.250	EC, CE	—
Ce–141	32.5	days	0.31	88.48	β^-, CE	0.43, 0.58
Ce–143	33	hr	0.95	11.07	β^-, CE	1.09, 1.38
Pr–142	19.2	hr	10	100	β^-	0.58, 2.15
Nd–147	11.1	days	1.8	17.18	β^-	0.37, 0.81
Nd–149	2.0	hr	3.7	5.72	β^-	1.5
Nd–151	15	min	3.0	5.60	β^-	1.93
Sm–145	1	year	<2	3.16	EC, CE	—
Sm–151	90	years		7.47	β^-	0.076
Sm–153	1.96	days	140	26.63	β^-	0.65, 0.72
Sm–155	23.5	min	5.5	22.53	β^-	1.50, 1.63
Eu–152m	9.2	hr	1400	47.77	β^-, β^+, EC	β^- 1.87, β^+ 0.90
Eu–152	13	years	7200	47.77	β^-, β^+, EC	β^- 1.47, β^+ 0.72
Eu–154	16	years	420	52.23	β^-, CE	0.15, 1.84
Gd–153	236	days	<125	0.20	EC, CE	—

Prominent photon energies and their abundance per 100 Beta disintegrations, energies in MeV	Saturation activity,* dpm/μg of element	Specific activity,* 1 hr irradiation, dpm/μg of element
.60 (98) 0.72 (10) 1.69 (46)	3.1×10^5	1.5×10^2
082 (100) 0.213 (100)		
07 (2) 0.51 (13) 0.57 (87)		
089 (100) 0.159 (100)	7.7×10^3	2.3
035 (100) 0.110 (100)	6.5×10^4	3.5×10^1
059 (2) 0.089 (100) 0.66	4.8×10^3	1.5
42 (0.8)	7.9×10^4	6.1×10^3
106 (100)	1.3×10^3	1.4
027 (96) 0.46 (15) 1.09 (10)	1.2×10^4	5.8×10^3
182 (22)	$<7.9 \times 10^2$	$<2.0 \times 10^1$
147 (94) 0.45 (23) 1.12 (8)	2.2×10^4	1.8×10^4
45 (17) 0.54 (2) 0.99 (0.5)	1.6×10^6	1.3×10^6
19 0.24	1.9×10^4	7.6×10^2
058 0.145 0.170		
040 (100) 0.196 (100)	$<2.7 \times 10^4$	$<1.1 \times 10^2$
164 (100)	$<5.7 \times 10^4$	$<1.5 \times 10^2$
233 (100)	$<3.8 \times 10^5$	$<4.9 \times 10^3$
081 (100) 0.160 (0.1)	1.5×10^4	8.6×10^1
53 (85)	$<1.5 \times 10^4$	$<1.4 \times 10^4$
250 (97) 0.61 (3)	5.7×10^3	4.5×10^2
	3.8×10^3	3.8×10^3
127 (28)	4.8×10^3	1.0×10^3
57 (13) 0.60 (97) 0.80 (94)	1.0×10^7	3.6×10^2
12 0.22 0.50	2.7×10^3	7.3
012 (100) 0.276 (100)	1.9×10^3	3.5×10^1
082 (25) 0.300 (25) 0.360 (69)	3.6×10^3	<1
27 (100)	1.3×10^4	3.4×10^2
662 (100)	1.0×10^4	1.0×10^4
166 (54) 1.43 (19)	9.4×10^4	3.7×10^4
33 (35) 0.49 (44) 0.81 (40) 1.60 (88)	2.2×10^6	4.0×10^4
255 (11)	3.0×10^2	6.6
010 (100) 0.44 (3)	3.4×10^3	2.7×10^2
166 (100)	3.9×10^2	<1
146 (70)	7.1×10^4	7.1×10^1
057 (80) 0.29 (43) 0.661 (10)	2.7×10^4	5.9×19^2
57 (4)	2.7×10^6	9.8×10^4
091 (29) 0.53 (15)	7.8×10^4	2.2×10^2
00 0.21 0.44	5.3×10^4	1.6×10^4
100 0.42	4.2×10^4	4.0×10^4
061 (92) 0.48	$<1.5 \times 10^4$	<1
020 (1)		
070 (40) 0.103 (78)	8.9×10^6	1.4×10^5
104 (96) 0.246 (4)	3.0×10^5	2.5×10^5
122 (13) 0.56 (24) 0.84 (11)	1.6×10^8	1.3×10^7
22 (62) 0.34 (26) 1.41 (25)	8.2×10^5	5.0×10^3
23 (88) 0.72 (21) 1.28 (42)	5.2×10^7	2.6×10^2
069 (2) 0.097 (21) 0.103 (25)	$<6 \times 10^4$	<8

Product Nuclide	Half-life		Isotopic σ_{ac}, barns	Isotopic Abundance, %	Decay modes	Maximum Beta Ray energy, MeV
Gd–159	18	hr	4	24.87	β^-	0.59, 0.95
Gd–161	3.7	min	0.8	21.90	β^-	1.60
Tb–160	73	days	>22	100	β^-, CE	0.56
Dy–157	8.2	hr		0.052	EC	—
Dy–159	144	days	96	0.090	EC	—
Dy–165m	1.25	min	510	28.18	β^-, IT	0.87
Dy–165	2.3	hr	2100	28.18	β^-	1.19, 1.28
Ho–166m	>30	years	>0.007	100	β^-	0.18, 0.28, 1.1
Ho–166	1.14	days	60	100	β^-	1.76, 1.84
Er–163	1.2	hr	2.03	0.136	EC	—
Er–165	10	hr	1.65	1.56	EC	—
Er–169	9.4	days	2.0	27.07	β^-, CE	0.34
Er–171	7.5	hr	9	14.88	β^-	0.5, 1.05
Tm–170	129	days	130	100	β^-	0.88, 0.96
Yb–169	32	days	11000	0.140	EC, CE	—
Yb–175	4.2	days	60	31.84	β^-	0.47
Yb–177	1.9	hr	5.5	12.73	β^-, CE	1.40
Lu–176m	3.7	hr	35	97.40	β^-	1.1, 1.2
Lu–177	6.8	days	4000	2.60	β^-	0.50
Hf–175	70	days	1500	0.18	EC	—
Hf–180m	5.5	hr	65	13.8	IT, CE	—
Hf–181	45	days	10	35.44	β^-, CE	0.41
Ta–182m	16.5	min	0.030	99.99	IT	—
Ta–182	115	days	19	99.99	β^-	0.51
W–181	145	days	10	0.135	EC	—
W–185m	1.7	min		30.6	IT	—
W–185	70	days	2.1	30.6	β^-	0.43
W–187	1.0	days	34	28.4	β^-	0.63, 1.31
Re–186	3.75	days	120	37.07	β^-, EC	0.93, 1.07
Re–188m	20	min		62.93	IT, CE	—
Re–188	17	hr	75	62.93	β^-	1.96, 2.12
Os–185	94	days	<200	0.018	EC	—
Os–187m	1.62	days		1.59		
Os–189m	5.7	hr		13.3	IT, CE	—
Os–190m	10	min		16.1	IT, CE	—
Os–191m	14	hr		26.4	IT	—
Os–191	15	days	8	26.4	β^-	0.14
Os–193	1.33	days	1.6	41.0	β^-	1.14
Ir–192m	1.4	min	260	38.5	β^-, IT, CE	0.1
Ir–192	74	days	700	38.5	β^-, EC	0.53, 0.67
Ir–194	19	hr	130	61.5	β^-	1.90, 2.24
Pr–191	3.0	days	90	0.012	EC	—
Pt–193m	4.4	days	8	0.78	IT, CE	—
Pt–195m	3.5	days	1.2	32.9	IT, CE	—
Pt–197m	1.3	hr		25.4	IT, CE	—
Pt–197	18	hr	0.87	25.4	β^-	0.48, 0.67
Pt–199	30	min	3.9	7.2	β^-	1.7

Prominent photon energies and their abundance per 100 Beta disintegrations, energies in MeV	Saturation activity,* dpm/μg of element	Specific activity,* 1 hr irradiation, dpm/μg of element
(19)	2.3×10^5	9.2×10^3
7 0.078 0.102	4.1×10^4	4.1×10^4
8 (3C) 0.876 (33) 0.964 (35)	$>5.1 \times 10^6$	$>2.3 \times 10^3$
4 0.061 0.083		
8 (25) 0.36 (0.01)	1.9×10^4	3.8
8 (97) 0.36 (3)	3.3×10^7	3.3×10^7
5 (3) 0.27 (1) 0.36 (2)	1.3×10^8	3.9×10^7
0 0.184 0.280	$>1.6 \times 10^3$	>0.01
0 (48) 1.38 (1)	1.3×10^7	3.4×10^5
1.1	6.0×10^2	2.7×10^2
e	5.6×10^3	3.9×10^2
8 (42)	1.2×10^5	3.7×10^2
1 (22) 0.29 (23) 0.31 (69)	3×10^5	2.7×10^4
4 (35)	2.8×10^7	6.4×10^3
3 0.064 0.11	3.2×10^6	2.9×10^3
4 (3) 0.28 (5) 0.40 (9)	4.0×10^6	2.8×10^4
7 (7) 1.08 (2) 1.23 (2)	1.5×10^5	5.0×10^4
9	7.0×10^6	1.3×10^6
(3) 0.21 (7)	2.1×10^7	8.4×10^4
3 (75)	5.4×10^5	2.4×10^2
3 (100) 0.216 (100) 0.332 (100)	1.9×10^6	2.5×10^5
3 (40) 0.35 (13) 0.482 (81)	7.3×10^5	6.8×10^2
(55)	6.0×10^3	5.7×10^3
0 (56) 1.12 (33) 1.22 (28)	3.8×10^6	1.0×10^4
6 (0.1) 0.152 (0.2)	2.8×10^3	<1
0.17 0.295		
e	1.3×10^5	5.7×10^1
4 (10) 0.48 (28) 0.68 (32)	1.9×10^6	5.7×10^4
3 (2) 0.137 (23) 0.63 (0.4)	8.7×10^6	7.0×10^4
4 0.105		
5 (9) 0.63 (1)	9.2×10^6	4.6×10^5
(80) 0.87 (7)	$<7 \times 10^3$	<2.2
0 (100)		
9 0.187 0.36		
4 (100)		
2 (100) 0.129 (100)	4.0×10^5	8.4×10^2
3 (35) 0.281 (12)	1.2×10^5	2.8×10^3
8 (100)	1.9×10^7	1.9×10^7
(30) 0.31 (29) 0.32 (83) 0.47 (53)	5.0×10^7	2.0×10^4
9 (5) 0.33 (24) 0.64 (6)	1.5×10^7	5.7×10^5
3 0.51 0.62	2.0×10^3	2.0×10^1
3 (100) 0.135 (100)	1.2×10^4	8.4×10^1
0 (100)	7.2×10^4	6.4×10^2
(100)		
7 (99) 0.191 (5) 0.28 (1)	4.0×10^4	1.6×10^3
7 0.32 0.54	5.1×10^4	4.1×10^4

Product Nuclide	Half-life	Isotopic σ_{ac}, barns	Isotopic Abundance, %	Decay modes	Maximu Beta Ra energy, M
Au–198	2.70 days	98.8	100	β^-, CE	0.28, 0.96,
Hg–197m	1.00 days	420	0.146	IT, CE, EC	—
Hg–197	2.71 days	880	0.146	CE, EC	—
Hg–199m	43 min	0.018	10.2	IT, CE	—
Hg–203	47 days	3.8	29.80	β^-	0.21
Hg–205	5.2 min	0.43	6.85	β^-	1.4, 1.62
Tl–204	3.9 years	8	29.50	β^-, EC	0.77
Tl–206	4.3 min	0.10	70.50	β^-	1.51
Pb–209	3.3 hr	0.0006	52.3	β^-	0.63
Bi–210	5.01 days	0.019	100	β^-, α	1.16
Th–233	22.1 min	7.33	100	β^-	1.23
U–235m	26.2 min	90	0.0057	IT	—
U–237	6.75 days	6	not in nat. U	β^-	0.25
U–239	23.5 min	2.74	99.3	β^-	1.21

*Thermal neutron flux of 1×10^{12} n cm^{-2} sec^{-1}

minent photon energies and their abundance per 100 Beta isintegrations, energies in MeV	Saturation activity,* dpm/μg of element	Specific activity,* 1 hr irradiation, dpm/μg of element
2 (99) 0.69 (1) 1.09 (0.2)	1.8×10^7	2.0×10^5
4 (96) 0.165 (96)	1.1×10^5	3.3×10^3
7 (100) 0.191 (1)	2.3×10^5	2.5×10^3
8 (100) 0.368 (100)	3.2×10^2	2.0×10^2
9 (100)	2.0×10^5	1.3×10^2
5	5.2×10^3	5.2×10^3
	4.2×10^5	8.4
	1.3×10^4	1.3×10^4
	5.4×10^1	1.1×10^1
	3.3×10^3	2.0×10^1
9 0.087 0.45	1.1×10^6	1.0×10^6
1 (100)	2.0×10^3	1.7×10^3
0 (36) 0.21 (24)	—	
4 (84)	1.1×10^6	9.2×10^5

Parent Nuclide	Reaction and cross section, mb				Product Nuclide	Half-life	Isotopic abundance of parent, %	De mo
	n, γ	n, p	n, α	n, 2n				
B–11			34		Li–8	0.83 sec	81.2	β^-, α
N–14				5	N–13	10.0 min	99.63	β^+
O–16		90			N–16	7.3 sec	99.59	β^-
F–19		135			O–19	29.4 sec	100	β^-
F–19				61	F–18	1.87 hr	100	β^+, E
Na–23		34			Ne–23	40.2 sec	100	β^-
Mg–24		190			Na–24	14.97 hr	78.60	β^-
Mg–25		45			Na–25	1.0 min	10.11	β^-
Al–27		70			Mg–27	9.45 min	100	β^-
Al–27			110		Na–24	14.97 hr	100	β^-
Si–28		220			Al–28	2.30 min	92.27	β^-
Si–29		100			Al–29	6.56 min	4.68	β^-
Si–30			80		Mg–27	9.45 min	3.05	β^-
P–31		77			Si–31	2.62 hr	100	β^-
P–31		150			Al–28	2.30 min	100	β^-
S–34		85			P–34	12.4 sec	4.215	β^-
S–34		140			Si–31	2.62 hr	4.215	β^-
Cl–35				4	Cl–34m	33.2 min	75.4	β^+,
Cl–37		28			S.–37	5.0 min	24.6	β^-
Cl–37			190		P–34	12.4 sec	24.6	β^-
K–39				10	K–38	7.7 min	93.08	β^+
K–41		80			Ar–41	1.83 hr	6.91	β^-
K–41			50		Cl–38	37.3 min	6.91	β^-
V–51		27			Ti–51	5.79 min	99.76	β^-
Cr–52		70			V–52	3.77 min	83.76	β^-
Mn–55			30		V–52	3.77 min	100	β^-
Fe–56		110			Mn–56	2.58 hr	91.68	β^-
Co–59			31		Mn–56	2.58 hr	100	β^-
Cu–63				500	Cu–62	9.8 min	69.1	β^+
Cu–65				1000	Cu–64	12.9 hr	30.9	β^-, β
Cu–65	6.2				Cu–66	5.1 min	30.9	β^-
Zn–64		390			Cu–64	12.9 hr	48.89	β^-, β
Zn–64				220	Zn–63	38.3 min	48.89	β^+, E
Zn–66		100			Cu–66	5.1 min	27.81	β^-
Ga–69			39		Cu–66	5.1 min	60.2	β^-

ax. Beta-y energy, MeV	Prominent photon energies and their abundance per 100 Beta disintegrations, energies in MeV	Activity, dpm/μg of element		
		Saturation	1 Hour	5 minutes
	none	93	93	93
	none	13	13	4
10.4	6.13 (73) 7.12 (5)	204	204	204
, 4.60	0.200 (96) 1.36 (54)	258	258	258
	none	116	37	4
, 4.39	0.44 (32) 1.65 (1)	54	54	54
	1.37 (100) 2.75 (100)	222	10	<1
3.7	0.40 (15) 0.58 (15) 0.98 (15) 1.61 (6.5)	7	7	7
, 1.75	0.84 (70) 1.02 (30)	94	94	30
	1.37 (100) 2.75 (100)	147	7	<1
	1.78 (100)	263	263	211
2.5	1.28 (85) 2.43 (15)	6	6	2.5
, 1.75	0.84 (100) 1.02 (30)	3	3	1
	1.26 (0.07)	90	21	2
	1.78 (100)	175	175	142
5.1	2.1 (25) 4.0 (0.2)	4	4	4
	1.26 (0.07)	7	2	<1
	1.16 (18) 2.10 (43) 3.22 (7)	3	2	<1
4.7	3.1 (90)	7	7	3.5
5.1	2.1 (25) 4.0 (0.2)	48	48	48
	2.16 (100)	9	9	3
	1.29 (99)	5	2	<1
2.8, 4.8	1.60 (31) 2.15 (47)	3	2	<1
, 2.13	0.32 (96) 0.61 (1) 0.93 (4)	19	19	9
	1.44 (100)	41	41	25
	1.44 (100)	20	20	12
, 1.05, 2.86	0.82 (99) 1.77 (23) 2.06 (14)	65	16	2
, 1.05, 2.86	0.82 (99) 1.77 (23) 2.06 (14)	19	5	<1
	0.66 (2) 0.85 (1) 1.18 (1) 1.35 (1)	197	197	59
.57, β^+ 0.66	1.34 (1) 0.51 (AN)	176	10	<1
, 2.63	1.04 (9)	1	1	<1
.57, β^+ 0.66	1.34 (1) 0.51 (AN)	106	6	<1
	0.96 (8) 1.89 (4) 2.60 (0.5)	59	41	6
, 2.63	1.04 (9)	15	15	8
, 2.63	1.04 (9)	12	12	6

Parent Nuclide	Reaction and cross section, mb				Product Nuclide	Half-life	Isotopic abundance of parent, %	Dec mod
	n, γ	n, p	n, α	n, 2n				
Ga–69				550	Ga–68	1.13 hr	60.2	β+, EC
Ga–71				700	Ga–70	20.2 min	39.8	β−
Ge–70		130			Ga–70	20.2 min	20.55	β−
Ge–70				700	Ge–69	36.9 hr	20.55	β+, EC
Ge–74			15		Zn–71	2.2 min	36.74	β−
Ge–76				1800	Ge–75	1.4 hr	7.67	β−
As–75		12			Ge–75	1.4 hr	100	β−
Se–82				1500	Se–81m	57 min	9.19	IT, Cl
Br–79				1100	Br–78	6.4 min	50.52	β+
Br–81			100		As–78	1.5 hr	49.48	β−
Br–81				800	Br–80m	4.58 hr	49.48	IT, Cl
Rb–87			40		Br–84	30 min	27.85	β−
Sr–88			60		Kr–85m	4.36 hr	82.56	β−, IT
Sr–88		18			Rb–88	17.8 min	82.56	β−
Zr–90				80	Zr–89	4.4 min	51.46	β+, IT,
Mo–92				190	Mo–91	15.5 min	15.86	β+
Mo–97		110			Nb–97	1.2 hr	9.45	β−
Ru–96				480	Ru–95	1.65 hr	5.7	β+, EC
Rh–103			60		Tc–100	15.7 sec	100	β−
Pd–105		700			Rh–105	36 hr	22.6	β−
Pd–110				2000	Pd–109	13.6 hr	13.5	β−, Cl
Ag–107				550	Ag–106	24 min	51.35	β+, EC
Ag–109				800	Ag–108	2.4 min	48.65	β−
Sb–121				750	Sb–120	16.5 min	57.25	β+, EC
Te–128				800	Te–127	9.4 hr	31.79	β−
Te–130				600	Te–129	1.1 hr	34.49	β−
I–127			18		Sb–124m2	21 min	100	β−, IT
Ce–140			12		Ba–137m	2.60 min	88.48	IT, Cl
Pr–141				2100	Pr–140	3.4 min	100	β+, EC
Gd–160				1500	Gd–159	18 hr	21.90	β−
Ta–181				900	Ta–180m	8.15 hr	99.99	β−, EC
Pt–198				2800	Pt–197	18 hr	7.2	β−
Au–197				2600	Au–196	5.5 days + 14 hr	100	β−, EC
Th–232				1200	Th–231	1.04 days	100	β−
U–238				700	U–237	6.75 days	99.3	β−

lax. Beta-ray energy, MeV	Prominent photon energies and their abundance per 100 Beta disintegrations, energies in MeV	Activity, dpm/μg of element		
		Saturation	1 Hour	5 Minutes
	0.81 1.07 (4) 1.24	172	79	9
	1.04 (1)	144	130	23
	1.04 (1)	13	12	2
, 1.21	0.090 0.388 0.576 0.870	72	1	<1
	0.51 (100)	3	3	2
, 1.18	0.26 (11)	69	28	3
, 1.18	0.26 (11)	6	3	<1
	0.103	63	34	4
	0.046 0.108	252	252	108
4.1	0.62 (42) 0.70 (11) 1.31 (10)	22	8	<1
	0.037 (100) 0.049 (100)	181	27	2
, 2.53, 4.68	0.27 0.35 0.43 0.47	5	4	<1
	0.15 (74) 0.31 (22)	20	3	<1
, 2.52	0.90 (9) 1.86 (15)	6	6	1
	0.59 (93) 1.5 (7)	16	16	9
	none	11	10	2
	0.69 (99) 1.02 (1)	4	2	<1
	0.145 0.340 0.460 1.11	10	3	<1
3.4	0.54 0.60	21	21	21
, 0.56	0.108 0.32 (20) 0.55	54	1	<1
	0.088 (100)* 0.30	93	5	<1
, 1.96	0.51 (18)	95	81	14
	0.43 (0.2) 0.63 (1)	130	130	104
	1.18 (1)	128	122	26
	0.42 (0.8)	72	5	<1
, 1.45	0.027 (96) 0.46 (15) 1.09 (10)	59	40	3
	0.018	5	5	<1
	0.662 (100)	3	3	2
	none	540	540	367
, 0.95	0.36 (19)	76	3	<1
, 0.70	0.093 (41) 0.102 (2)	180	16	1
0.67	0.077 (99) 0.191 (5) 0.28 (1)	37	2	<1
	0.331 0.354 0.43	478	mixed	yield
4, 0.218	0.026 0.084 0.099	187	6	<1
	0.060 (36) 0.21 (24)	106	<1	<1

ABBREVIATIONS

σ	nuclear cross section; 10^{-24} cm^2 (unless otherwise shown)
μc	microcurie
μg	microgram
b	barn; 10^{-24} cm^2
c	curie
dpm	disintegrations per minute
dps	disintegrations per second
e	electron
EC	electron capture
hr	hour
min	minute
mb	millibarn; 10^{-27} cm^2
mc	millicurie
n	neutron
sec	second
SF	spontaneous fission

INDEX*

* In this index, "neutron activation" refers to thermal neutron activation only.

133

OTHER TITLES IN THE SERIES ON
ANALYTICAL CHEMISTRY